D1068386

Trees of Parks and Gardens

TREES

of Parks and Gardens

Text by

J. POKORNÝ

Illustrations by

V. CHOC

SPRING BOOKS

Translated by Olga Kuthanová
Designed and Produced by ARTIA for
SPRING BOOKS
Published by the Hamlyn Publishing Group Limited
London · New York · Sydney · Toronto
Hamlyn House, Feltham, Middlesex, England
Reprinted 1969, 1970

ISBN 0 600 03869 6
Printed in Czechoslovakia by TSNP Martin

Trees and Man

Woods and forests cover most of the surface of our planet and greatly influence its appearance. Anyone who has seen deserts, or large coalfields covered with slag heaps instead of trees, or new volcanic islands with no life at all, will appreciate how plants, and above all trees, beautify and soften the harsh outlines of the earth's surface.

But trees and other plants are not only important for their beauty. They are essential to civilization and to life itself. Without plants, which are capable of transforming inorganic into organic matter, no animals could exist. One of the essential conditions for the life of primitive man was the forest, which provided him not only with food, but also with fuel and shelter. There are many examples, as we are finding out today, where the disappearance of forests and devastation of the land were directly linked with the disappearance of ancient cultures and empires. It is not necessary, however, to go that far back into history to realize the importance of trees to mankind. It is only a few generations ago that trees and wood were part of man's life, one might say from the cradle to the grave—from the wooden cradle to the wooden coffin. Wood was used to build dwellings, to make furniture, utensils, tools, vehicles, primitive weapons, and until almost the end of the 18th century it was the only source of heat and energy. Today's great advances in chemistry produce plastics which can in many instances replace wood, but they are at the same time finding new ways in which this traditional and ever-popular material can be used.

The value of trees and forests does not rest only in the wealth of timber they represent. Today it is known that they play an important role in water management and in preventing soil erosion, as well as in keeping the atmosphere of our cities clean.

Structure and Nutrition of Trees

Trees are the largest of plant organisms, with an extremely long life-span—several times that of man. The areas on which man grows plants for his food were previously covered with forests, and the forest would again reclaim them if man were to cease his tilling of the soil. In the tropical regions especially, where the conditions for their growth are best, forests quickly repossess not only abandoned fields, but even whole villages and towns. There are many examples of where this has happened in Central America, South-east Asia and Africa. Only in those places where there is insufficient rainfall and extreme temperatures, or severe winters and frozen ground, are trees restricted in their growth, only there do they relinquish their role to grasslands, shrubs or succulent plants.

The chief distinguishing characteristic of a tree is the long woody main trunk, dividing some distance above the ground to form a crown of a few thick branches further divided into numerous smaller branches. In conifers, which have leaves shaped like narrow needles, the trunk reaches to the very tip of the slender, conical crown. In broad-leaved trees it generally divides at one point into thick upward-growing branches, which divide further to form a crown which may be either ovate or round. These shapes provide the leaves with the greatest amount of light and air, assuring the best conditions for the nourishment of the tree. The tree is anchored in the ground by means of roots which also serve to supply it with water and dissolved mineral elements.

The leaves of broad-leaved trees consist of the stalk or petiole and a thin blade, which provides the greatest possible surface of contact with the air, for atmospheric carbon dioxide is the tree's main source of food. During the day trees are able to build up carbohydrates (starch and sugars) from carbon dioxide and water, with the aid of chlorophyll, a green substance which is present in the cells of the leaves. This complex compound enables the tree to utilize the radiant energy from sunlight for the production of its own organic food material. Since the amount of carbon dioxide in the air is very low (0.03 per cent), the tree has to process great quantities of air and this must take place on the greatest possible leaf surface. To provide this, the leaves are very thin in relation to their bulk, and a mature tree has several tens or hundreds of thousands of them. To make the most of the energy in sunlight, they are spread out as much as possible, both by the complex network of branches and by the varying lengths and positions of the leaf-stalks.

The shape and structure of the leaves of conifers (known as needles) differ. They are constructed to minimize transpiration (water loss), being long and narrow in outline, rhomboid, semi-circular or elliptical in cross-section. This is an efficient adaptation to their environment, for conifers are trees of the north and of mountain areas, where the climate is harsh and the summer short. To make the most of this brief period and not lose time in producing new leaves, most species retain their foliage throughout the winter. To be able to survive the snow, frost and lack of water, the leaves have a specialized shape and structure. They are distinguished by thick-walled cells, and in many cases their surface is protected by a waxy layer; they are able to close their stomata (transpiration and respiration pores) so perfectly that in winter the conifer loses less water through evaporation than a leafless broad-leaved tree. With the arrival of sunny weather in spring, conifers immediately begin to assimilate nutritive elements from the soil, and to transpire through their leaves even though everything around them is still blanketed with snow and the nights bring sub-zero temperatures.

Leaves differ with the species and are distinguished by the shape of the leaf-blade, the leaf-margin and the pattern of veins. They may be *simple*, with a single blade (which may be lobed) or *compound*, with three or more blades (leaflets) on a common stalk (rachis). When a number of leaflets radiate from the end of the rachis, the leaf is termed *palmately compound*; when the leaflets are attached laterally to the rachis, it is *pinnately compound*, either *odd-pinnate* or *even-pinnate*, depending on the number of leaflets. In some species with large leaves (Honey Locust, Kentucky Coffee-tree), the leaflets are divided even further *(bipinnately compound)*. The leaf-margin may be either *entire* (smooth) or *serrated* or *lobed* in various ways. Another important distinguishing character is the arrangement of the leaves on the twig; they grow either in opposite or alternate positions. The arrangement of the buds coincides with that of the leaves, so that this characteristic can be used to distinguish trees even in winter.

Most European broad-leaved trees are deciduous, discarding their leaves in the autumn. Only in southern and temperate western Europe do some species have green leaves throughout the year, e.g. the Common Holly, the Laurel and the Holm Oak. In autumn the organic matter manufactured by the leaves is concentrated into the body of the tree and the colour of the leaves changes. This is because the green chlorophyll decomposes, so that the usually hidden red and yellow substances, called carotenoids, now predominate, while at the same time there is an increase in the amount of anthocyanin (a pigment which is blue in the conditions of the cell sap). The autumn coloration is characteristic for many types of woody plants; for example, in the poplars, the birches, the Common Ash, and the Maidenhair Tree the leaves are yellow, in the Beech they are orange-brown, in the Red Oak and Wild Service Tree they are red, and in the Staghorn Sumach and Spindle Tree purplish green.

The leaves of some trees change their colour during the autumn months from yellow to red to brown. They separate from the twig and fall to the ground, thus returning to the soil a large part of the minerals taken from it. The shedding of leaves in the autumn is a result of the climate in this zone, where in winter the tree reduces its life processes to the minimum and so reduces the water in its tissues to survive the cold months as well as possible.

Conifers do not shed their leaves in the autumn, but equally they do not retain them throughout their lifetime. They are replaced by new ones after two to ten years, depending on the type of tree and on the environment. The interval in the case of the Scots Pine, for example, is shorter than in the Norway Spruce, which when growing at lower altitudes sheds its needles more often than the same species found farther north and on high mountains.

Another element essential to the life of woody plants is water and the dissolved minerals it contains. The tree absorbs it from the soil through its roots, chiefly through the young parts of the root and root hairs.

This solution of nutrient substances (sap) must now be lifted against the pull of gravity to the top of the trunk and out to the furthest branches to supply the leaves; this can amount to a distance of hundreds of feet in the tallest trees. The sap is conveyed in a system of minute tubes (vascular system) continuous throughout the whole tree. These form the fibrous part of the roots, a series of layers visible as rings on the trunk and branches when they are cut across, and the stalks and veins of the leaves; the layers mentioned grow annually, and it is usually the youngest, outer layer which is the operational one. The energy required to lift the sap to these great heights is considerable. In the roots, pressure is built up by osmosis—the flow of a weaker solution into a more concentrated one through a membrane such as a plant cell-wall (called a semi-permeable membrane) until the concentration of dissolved substances is the same on both sides of the membrane.

In the trunk, the main force which serves to transport the water is the cohesion of the water column to the walls of the tiny vessels, and evaporation at the leaves, which causes a partial vacuum which tends to pull the sap up. The individual cells of the woody tissues take the amount of water they need for the various chemical processes and the remainder is conducted to the leaves. Here some of the water is used in the manufacture of sugar, but a large part still remains unused. Woody plants absorb more water than they can use, since they mainly require the minerals dissolved in it, and the excess is eliminated by transpiration from the leaves. This process consists of the evaporation of water under the regulation of a system of pores which can be expanded or closed; it can also be limited by the furling or drooping of the leaves. On the other hand, movement of the leaves can increase the rate of evaporation. The evaporation of water during transpiration gives the further advantage that the leaf surface is being constantly cooled, so that the leaf tissues are not exposed to high temperatures.

The amount of water transpired by an individual tree or forest into the atmosphere is very large, varying, of course, not only according to the sizes and species of the plants, but also according to the conditions of the environment —soil moisture, relative humidity of the air, temperature, force of the wind, etc. The rate of transpiration of broad-leaved trees is several times greater than that of conifers. An exceptionally high rate is exhibited by poplars, Aspen, alders, birches and the Common Ash.

Let us examine the structure of the trunk more closely. In the centre is a narrow shaft of pith composed of living cells with cellulose walls (parenchymatous cells); around this the xylem or woody element, made up of the concentric circles of the annual layers of water-conducting tubes; then a thin layer of phloem which consists of tubes for conducting foodstuffs; on the outside is the bark. Between the xylem and the phloem is a thin layer called the cambium, consisting of several layers of thin-walled cells which during the period of growth rapidly divide to form new xylem on the inner layer and new phloem on the outer. Growth of wood occurs annually because in temperate areas the cambium does not function at the same rate throughout the year and produces various different types of wood cells. In spring, during the period of intensive growth, the cambium produces broad, thin-walled cells known as springwood, whereas the cells produced in summer are narrow and thick-walled and are called late wood; during the winter months the cambium ceases to function. The strip of compact late wood can be easily distinguished from the following year's strip of springwood, so that on the cross-section, as on the top of a tree-stump, one can clearly observe the annual growth by the growth rings and thus also determine the tree's age. The width of the annual layer is proportional to the amount of manufactured plant food and corresponds more or less to the weather in the given year; in a good year it will be broad, while a narrow growth ring reflects the unfavourable influence of a dry year, a period of severe frosts, etc. This correlation is being applied today by the new science of dendrochronology to determine, by examining the rings in trees hundreds or thousands of years old, the pattern and variations in the weather, the alternation of dry and wet years, of a time when the science of meteorology was still unknown. Trees growing in the tropics, where the period of vegetation is continuous, do not possess visible growth rings.

In older trees only the outer, younger portion of wood is physiologically active; the inner, central portion consists of non-living cells and is known as heartwood. It is the tissues of the outer portion, called sapwood, which conduct the water and other important substances to the top of the tree. In broad-leaved trees this function is performed by the tracheae—broad tubular xylem cells which in cross-section appear to the naked eye as minute pores. In conifers these tubular cells are narrower and are called tracheids.

In the cells and cell walls of heartwood are stored various organic and inorganic substances (e.g. tannins, resins, silicon dioxide) which increase the specific weight of the wood. In some trees, e.g. Yew, larches, pines, the Common Oak, the heartwood is also distinguished from the sapwood by its darker colour. Heartwood is much more durable and of higher quality and in the tropics, where felled timber is much more prone to rapid decay and insect damage, the sapwood is hacked off on the spot and only the heartwood is shipped for further processing.

The xylem, or woody portion of the tree, is encircled by a thin layer of phloem whose main function is to carry away to the trunk and roots the excess organic materials manufactured by the leaves. It consists mainly of sieve tubes made up of long tubular cells with perforated partitions. The surface of the trunk is covered with bark, which protects it from undue evaporation and sudden changes in temperature. The vast importance of this protection becomes clear when one realizes what great quantities of water are conducted through the outer woody tissues.

On the bark can often be seen small wartlike patches, either round or slit-like in shape, which differ in colour from the surrounding bark. These are called lenticels and their function is aeration—the exchange of gases between the atmosphere and the stem tissues.

The bark, too, thickens every year with the addition of a thin, almost invisible layer. The thickness of the bark varies. In shade-living trees it is usually thin, in those exposed to the sun it is often very thick. The older, exterior bark layers cannot adapt themselves to the constant thickening of the trunk, which is why in most trees the bark is split in furrows or scales.

Reproduction

Trees multiply chiefly by sexual reproduction, in which the male and female gametes (sex cells) fuse and give rise to a new individual. The reproductive organs in woody plants are contained in the flowers, whose function is the production of seed. The male sex organ, called the stamen, consists of the anther, which produces the pollen, carried on a filament; the female organ, the pistil, comprises the ovary, style and stigma. In some trees the flowers are *unisexual*, i.e. the stamens and pistils occur in separate flowers; those containing both the male and female organs are termed *bisexual*. Unisexual flowers are to be found in all conifers and in most broad-leaved trees which are pollinated by wind-borne pollen, e.g. birches, alders, oaks, poplars. Species in which both male (or *staminate*) and female (or *pistillate*) flowers occur on the same tree are termed *monoecious*, those where the male flowers are borne on one individual and the female on another are termed *dioecious* (Common Yew, poplars, willows, etc.). The flowers of most trees are much less conspicuous and less brightly coloured than in shrubs and herbaceous plants. Since trees are generally pollinated by wind-borne pollen, the brightly coloured petals, which have evolved to attract insects, are either rudimentary or completely absent.

The method of pollination also influences to a certain extent the period of flowering of a given species. Wind-pollinated trees, such as the poplars, the Aspen, the alders and the Hornbeam, develop flowers early in spring before the crown is in leaf, when the pollen can be distributed much more easily; trees dependent on insects for pollination (limes, the Black Locust, hawthorns, etc.) flower later, when the leaves unfold.

Fertilization takes place when the pollen released from the anther and borne by the wind or insects is deposited on the stigma, germinates and one of the male gametes fuses with an egg-cell in the ovule situated in the ovary or on an ovuliferous scale of the female cone of the conifers. Wind-pollinated trees produce their pollen in enormous quantities because the chance of the pollen reaching the stigmas is small. When Scots Pines or Norway Spruces are in bloom, for example, a great golden cloud of pollen hangs above the stand and the surface of any puddles and ponds in the vicinity will be covered with the yellow dust. The pollen grains of most wind-pollinated woody plants have air-sacs which lighten them for easier movement in the air. Pollen grains can be carried for distances of five to ten miles or more. In trees where these air-sacs are absent (larches, the Douglas Fir, walnuts), pollination is not as successful; the pollen is carried only a distance of perhaps several yards, and the tree produces a large number of barren seeds. Trees pollinated by insects produce a much smaller quantity of pollen grains as most of them are reliably transferred to the stigma by the insect.

Woody plants are provided with means to prevent self-pollination, because individuals resulting from this method of propagation have less vitality or are entirely incapable of holding their own. One such device is the occurrence of male and female flowers on separate trees; where both are found on the same tree, the two sexes often have different periods of maturation.

The quantity of seeds produced depends not only on the number of flowers but also on the climatic conditions during the period of flowering and seed maturation. Frosts or rainy weather can destroy a part or all of the seed crop. Also, trees do not flower every year, for a large reserve supply of food is required to produce seeds and fruit and this must be accumulated by the plant over a certain period of time. The seed-bearing years of those trees which produce large seeds and require large food reserves (oaks, the Beech, walnuts) occur at intervals of from four to eight years. In harsher climates, for example at high altitudes or in northern regions where the accumulation of the necessary food supply takes a longer time, the seed-bearing intervals are also longer.

Trees usually only begin bearing seeds at a quite advanced age. Moreover, the seed-bearing age of trees growing in stands is usually ten to fifteen years later than that of individuals growing singly. Ten years is the seed-bearing age of solitary growing alders, birches, larches, thirty that of the maples, the Douglas Fir and the Norway Spruce, and about fifty that of the European Silver Fir and the Beech.

The number of seeds produced in a good year is enormous. One acre of forest, an area on which 2000 to 6000 seedlings are set out in forest planting, yields over one million seeds for a Scots Pine stand, two million for Norway Spruce between one and two million for Beech and up to forty million for birches. But these excessive yields are nature's defence against the great losses suffered by the seeds and the young plants. A great quantity of seeds is consumed by birds and animals, and many fall in places unsuitable to their growth, where they either do not germinate at all or die shortly after when the store of food in the seed is exhausted. Similarly, many young trees perish during their first years through drought or frost, are overpowered by grass or other plants, or are eaten by animals. After several years, less than one per cent is all that remains of the original abundant crop.

To ensure that the seeds land in a suitable, open space and do not merely fall to the ground beside the parent tree, where the prospects for their growth are poor, they are adapted for more or less widespread dispersal. Most species depend on the wind for this purpose and are either downy (willows, poplars), or have membranous wings (birches, elms, pines, spruces) or thick wings (maples, lime trees, hornbeams). The seeds of some other trees are disseminated by animals, mainly birds. These are generally from trees with fleshy, brightly coloured fruit which the birds eat, dispersing the seeds in their droppings (the Mountain Ash, Gean Cherry, Common Yew). In still another group (oaks, the Beech, walnuts etc.)the seeds form part of the diet of birds and mammals which eat the greater part, but occasionally forget the hoards they have tucked away in various places or else they drop some of the seeds while carrying them. Some fruits are covered with spines (the Beech, the Sweet Chestnut) which become attached in the fur of animals and are later dropped or rubbed off. Dispersal by means of animals would appear to be less effective than wind dispersal, but the history of tree migration in the wake of the retreating ice sheet in the period following the Ice Age indicates the contrary. Birches and the Scots Pine, the first pioneers to move northward, were followed by the rapid invasion of the Common Oak and the Hazel, whose heavy seeds fall only a few yards from the parent tree. Acorns are favourites of the jay and pigeon, hazel-nuts are eaten by the nutcracker, and these birds often carry them long distances in their bills, now and then dropping one along the way, so that the offspring may take root several hundred yards or even miles from the parent tree. That is how, over a period covering several generations, these trees made their way hundreds of miles to the north.

A less frequent phenomenon is the dispersal of tree seeds by water, as is the case in water plants. Of the European trees, water assists in dispersing the seeds of the alders, which also employ wind dispersal, and in the tropics one example is the Coconut Palm. In the case of the alders, the seeds possess air-sacs and can float on the surface for weeks, to be distributed far and wide during the spring floods.

If we take a closer look at the type of seed, its method of dispersal, and the biological characteristics of any tree, we will find that all these things are closely linked and have a direct bearing on each other. Thus, for instance, such pioneer trees as the birches, the Aspen, alders and pines, which colonize wide expanses of open country, bear a large number of seeds which are very light and adapted for flights of several hundred yards or even miles. Young trees can therefore be found growing in places where there is no other tree in sight. These trees are also well adapted to the climate of such situations. They are able to withstand heat and frost, require less fertile soil, and because of their rapid early growth are not killed by the surrounding grasses and weeds. They start to bear seeds at an early age, so that their offspring soon populate the surrounding area. Shade loving trees (the European Silver Fir, the Beech, lime trees), on the other hand, which when young require the shelter of the older parent stand, have heavier seeds which do not fall far.

In addition to sexual reproduction by way of seeds, there are some trees that multiply asexually; this is called vegetative reproduction. One example is the growth of new individuals from the roots of the parent tree, which in time may thus be surrounded by a whole group of young trees. This method is found in the Aspen, White Poplar, Black Locust, Staghorn Sumach and Blackthorn. The roots of these trees are generally spread out wide, and suckers may appear sixty or more feet from the trunk. These suckers are particularly abundant after the felling of the parent tree or the severing of one of its surface roots.

Another example of vegetative reproduction is stump suckers. This method is not very effective where man does not lend a hand because a new individual can spring up only in place of an old tree, from its stump or the remainder of its trunk. It is much more widespread in copses where the stands are renewed from stumps, and in the case of willows, poplars, the Common Yew and most ornamental shrubs which are grown directly from cuttings. Some trees multiply also by branches lying on the ground sending out roots and giving rise to new individuals. This method of reproduction is characteristic of the Norway Spruce growing in high mountain regions, the lime trees growing on stone debris, and the Arbor-vitae and other ornamental shrubs in parks. It is interesting to note that vegetative reproduction is more prevalent in trees growing in harsh environments, where the possibility of sexual reproduction is greatly decreased and occurs only at lengthy intervals.

Tree Growth and Attainable Age

The rate of growth of a tree during its lifetime can be illustrated by a graph which rises to a certain point, indicating the age when the plant shows the most marked growth, and then curves gradually downward until it levels off when the tree has attained its full growth. After this, though its height remains unchanged, the tree may grow in diameter and live to be several hundred years old. This growth curve is more or less the same for all trees, the rate and point of culmination varying according to the individual species.

Trees are divided roughly into three groups according to their rate of growth —fast, moderate and slow-growing. Those of the first group are distinguished by fast growth when young, with maximum growth at an early age, early termination of growth and, as a rule, a short life. Such trees do not attain great heights; on the contrary, the tallest trees are those which have only a slow or moderately fast growth. In the slow-growing group, the rate of change when young is slower, the upward tendency covers a longer period and the peak is attained later; the downward curve is less sharp and more protracted and the tree has a longer life span. The highest tree in the world may be a eucalyptus *Eucalyptus amygdalina*, which attains a height of almost 500 feet. Much better known for their gigantic proportions, however, are the big conifers of North America: the Wellingtonia *Sequoiadendron giganteum* and the Redwood *Sequoia sempervirens*, the greatest height attained by them being 360–420 feet. Heights of 260–300 feet are reached by some other American conifers, such as the Giant Fir, Noble Fir, Douglas Fir and Giant Pine. Of the European trees the tallest are the European Silver Fir, measuring over 200 feet, and the Norway Spruce, which may reach a height of more than 195 feet.

Fast-growing trees (alders, birches, poplars, larches, etc.) are usually also sun-loving, whereas slow-growing trees (firs, the Common Yew, the Beech) are shade-loving.

In most trees the annual increase in length is comparatively rapid and takes place within a period of three to four weeks. It begins at about the time the leaves unfold, is slow at first and then rapid (perhaps three-quarters of an inch a day), followed by one to two weeks of slower growth. It ends with the appearance of the terminal bud on the tip of the shoot. This method is characteristic of the Scots Pine, the Norway Spruce, Silver Fir, oaks, ashes and the Beech, their elongation being generally terminated by the end of June. There is, of course, another group of trees whose annual growth covers the entire vegetative period, i.e. three to four months. This group includes the poplars, alders, birches and the Dawn Redwood. Since growth begins early in spring, usually before the tree's assimilation organs are fully developed, the substances required for growth are taken from the previous year's store; the extent of growth is influenced mainly by the weather of the preceding year.

The case is somewhat different as regards growth in diameter which takes place throughout the entire vegetative season, from the time the tree puts out leaves until they fall in the autumn, and is influenced by the weather of the current year. In some trees this growth may be as much as an inch or more in one year. Great thickness is attained among European trees by the Plane Tree, the Sweet Chestnut, oaks, lime trees, the Sycamore, and of the conifers, the European Silver Fir and to a lesser extent the Norway Spruce. The Wellingtonia and Redwood reach as much as 33 feet in diameter.

The thickness of the trunk is naturally proportional also to the attainable age. In this, too, trees show marked differences; some are short-lived while others may live ten times longer. Short-lived trees have a more rapid life cycle—fast growth when they are young, early fruit-bearing and early ageing. Though called short-lived their life span is still longer than that of a man, being anywhere from 100 to 150 years. This age is attained by the Aspen, Sallow, birches and the Mountain Ash. Ages of 200 to 300 years are attained by the Black Poplar, hornbeams, willows, pines and larches, approximately 500 years by the Beech and Sycamore, and 700 years by the spruces and firs; the oldest trees in central and western Europe are some lime trees, the Common Oak and Common Yew, which are believed to be about 1000 years old. An even greater age is attained in the Mediterranean region by the Plane Tree, the Chestnut and the Cedar of Lebanon. On the American continent there are trees that are much older. As many as 2500 annual rings were counted on the stump of a Redwood, and some Wellingtonias are believed to be 3500 to 3800 years old. In the last decade a stand of Bristle-cone Pine *Pinus aristata* was discovered in the Rocky Mountains of Nevada, in which the oldest individuals had 4200 annual rings. The oldest tree in the Americas is the "Big Tree of Tule", growing in Santa Maria del Tule, Mexico, estimated to be 5000 to 6000 years old. It is a Mexican Swamp Cypress *Taxodium mucronatum*.

Natural Distribution and Introduction of Exotics

Every woody plant has a certain range which can be marked out on a map and is termed the natural distributional area. Knowledge of these areas is of great importance because it makes it possible to ascertain the requirements of individual trees as regards climate, moisture, soil fertility, etc., for they have been growing there for hundreds and thousands of years and have become adapted to the climate of the given locality. It also makes it possible to determine whether the tree prefers coastal or inland regions.

In individual parts of its range where the tree is exposed to differing conditions, it varies in its appearance as well as in its physiological characteristics. In species which have a wide range of distribution, one will find the occurrence of quite different local races, termed ecotypes. Thus, for example, the Scots Pine of northern Sweden, Finland and Lapland has a long, slender tapering crown which is not so liable to be weighted down with snow and makes the most of the rays of the low-lying sun. In the low elevations and dry climate of central Europe, the crowns of some other species of pines are broad to provide shade for the site. Likewise the Norway Spruce growing in mountains at high altitudes or in cold freezing valleys has a slender, narrow crown. Variations in climate are reflected in the onset of budding, different rhythm of vegetation and varying resistance to frost. Characteristics that have evolved over many generations under the influence of the environment are hereditary and are passed on to the offspring.

How the environment affects the form of the tree and shape of the crown is well illustrated by the difference between a tree grown in the open and one growing in a forest, where it has to compete with other trees. These differences are especially marked in shade-loving trees. For example, the Norway Spruce grown in the open is branched near the ground, since even the lowest branches have sufficient light. The trunk is conical and the tree's centre of gravity remains in the lower half, making it resistant to the force of the wind. When grown in a stand the lower branches die through lack of light, and the green crown is set high up the clear length of the trunk, which is only slightly conical with the centre of gravity located in its upper half. In this case the tree is protected from the force of the wind by the surrounding stand. If such a tree is suddenly left to stand alone in the open, not only does it suffer from the strong sunlight but it can soon become a victim of the wind.

A tree, of course, is not confined by the limits of its natural distributional range; it can grow elsewhere as well. After the Ice Age trees spread in the wake of the retreating ice sheet, establishing their present range; some species may not yet have found a region that would fully suit their needs. Other species as they spread met insurmountable barriers such as mountains and broad river valleys which lacked suitable conditions for their growth, though beyond them the environment was again favourable. Such barriers in Europe are the Alps and the Carpathians, which checked the further spread of many species, for example the Austrian Pine *Pinus nigra*, the Sweet Chestnut *Castanea sativa*, and the Turkey Oak *Quercus cerris*, which would have found the warm Rhineland and other regions north of the Alps favourable to their growth. The general pattern of distribution permits the conclusion that those trees growing as far north as the Arctic Circle (birches, pines, the Aspen, alders, the Norway Spruce) are frost-resistant, whereas trees whose centre of distribution is in southern Europe will be more sensitive to frost, and in more northern areas only warm and protected sites will prove favourable for their growth.

Trees from other regions or continents may be introduced into a new environment for their fruit or as a source of other products, to raise the yield of wood or to augment the assortment of ornamental plants. The introduction of new plants has been practised by mankind for many hundreds of years. It has been most widely practised in the past two or three centuries, when man settled the vast expanses of America and Asia. At first these trees and shrubs were often brought to the new lands as novelties to be planted in parks, but later economic reasons prevailed and exotics appeared in forest stands and in the open.

Unfortunately most plantings were set out without any plan and without sufficient knowledge of the ecology of the imported trees, with the result that most of these attempts ended in failure. On the other hand, several successful cases, for example the Eastern Cottonwood, Douglas Fir, Weymouth Pine, within several decades showed how economically important these trees could be. The end of the nineteenth and beginning of the twentieth centuries thus mark the beginning of a new stage—the planting of imported trees in woodlands with due consideration of their ecology, and with very promising results. In Great Britain, for example, in 1947, exotics were planted in woods covering about 600,000 acres; the chief species were Sitka Spruce (160,000 acres), Norway Spruce (130,000 acres), European Larch (127,000 acres), Japanese Larch (53,000 acres) and Douglas Fir (41,000 acres). Most plantings prosper and often such trees give twice the yield of native species. Today the economic aspect is forcing other European countries with a high standard of forestry to introduce and expand their plantings of exotics. Exotics, trees as well as shrubs, have found even wider application as ornamental plants in parks, gardens and city streets.

This practice has many supporters but also many who are opposed to it. The main reason for opposition is the fear of the spread of new diseases and of changing the characteristic appearance of the landscape. The first can be resolved by systematic checking of the imported seed and of the pests on new plantings. The second danger can be reduced to the minimum if the exotics are planted wisely and with forethought. Most imported trees are very similar to their relatives in the new environment, and the layman will have difficulty in distinguishing the Sitka Spruce and Douglas Fir from the familiar Norway Spruce or the Giant Fir and Caucasian Fir from the European Silver Fir. Besides, the Ice Age narrowed Europe's wide assortment of species and most of the genera found in America originally flourished in Europe as well, e.g. Redwood *Sequoia*, hemlocks *Tsuga*, hickories *Carya*, walnuts *Juglans* and Tulip-Tree *Liriodendron*. Gradual, planned augmentation of the current European assortment thus represents merely the remedying of the results of natural catastrophes and does not really go against the grain of nature's scheme. The main mountain ranges in Europe (Pyrenees, Alps, Carpathians) run from west to east, so that in the Ice Age they blocked the southward retreat of many tree species, which fell victim to the advancing ice sheet. In America, on the other hand, where the chief mountain ranges run north and south, the trees survived by moving south, returning once again to the more northerly regions when the time came. That is why those trees which perished in Europe survived on the American continent, and why genera occurring on both continents are much more plentiful in the New World.

PLATES

Maidenhair Tree or Ginkgo

Ginkgo biloba

The Maidenhair Tree, which Darwin called a living fossil, is the only existing species of the order Ginkgoales, whose members were numerous and widespread during the Mesozoic and Tertiary eras. It is a robust tree attaining a height of 90 to 110 ft and a diameter of more than 3 ft. The flowers are dioecious, the male and female flowers occurring on separate trees. The shape of the crown and the trunk differ with the sex: trees bearing male flowers have a straight, slender trunk and a narrow crown; in those with female flowers the crown is wide. The leaves are slender-stalked, fan-shaped, with two lobes and dichotomous venation. Those of young trees and vigorous growing shoots are alternate and deeply two-lobed. The leaves of older twigs are crowded in bunches and notched or jagged at the tip. The flowers are pollinated by the wind. The fruit of the Maidenhair is plum-shaped, just under an inch in diameter. While it is ripening (in September and October), the fleshy layer turns yellow and has an unpleasant odour; it encloses a hard grey-white stone with an oily edible kernel.

The Maidenhair is probably a native of eastern Asia but has never been found in the wild state. It owes its survival to Chinese and Japanese temple gardens where it was cultivated as a holy tree. It was introduced into Europe around 1730 and in Britain in 1754, and is cultivated today as an ornamental throughout Europe. In summer it is truly decorative with its grey-barked trunk and characteristic dark green leaves which turn golden yellow in autumn, the effect being heightened in female plants by the yellowish fruits. It is planted singly.

A light-living tree, it requires cool, moist and fertile soil. In the mild climate of central Europe it is comparatively resistant to frost, but in northern Europe it can suffer severely from frost. It does fairly well in cities and can be grown from seed or from cuttings, or propagated by layering and grafting.

Common or English Yew

Taxus baccata

The Yew is an evergreen conifer, widespread in most of Europe except the extreme north and east, growing locally in many areas. It grows very slowly and attains an age of more than one hundred years. It is a shrub or tree up to 60 ft high, with dense, spreading branches. The bark is reddish-brown and peels off in thin scales. The leaves, measuring less than an inch long and a tenth of an inch wide, are needle-like, flat, gradually pointed at the tip, dark green above, yellow-green below, and arranged in two opposite ranks on the twigs. The inconspicuous flowers appear early in spring (March); they are of two kinds, male and female, which grow on separate trees. In autumn the female plants produce fruits consisting of a brownish seed about a quarter of an inch long enveloped by a scarlet cup-shaped aril. The fruits are fleshy and sweet and attract birds, which eat them and disseminate the seeds over a wide range.

The Common Yew grows in the undergrowth of mixed broad-leaved woods from Britain to Transcaucasia, but has been diminishing in numbers over several centuries. This began with the large-scale felling of these trees in the Middle Ages when its flexible wood was widely used to make bows and furniture. The Common Yew is now protected by law in many countries, but it does not prosper in intensive management of forests. Today it is commonly cultivated in parks as an ornamental either for its bright colouring or its compact, pyramidal shape. In Britain it is often planted in churchyards. It is very resistant to the smoky atmosphere of cities and also stands up well to clipping so that it is often used for evergreen hedges and topiary. The bark, shoots, leaves and fruits (except the fleshy aril) of the Yew are poisonous, but forest animals, feeding on it in small quantities, suffer no ill effects. The wood is hard and compact, coloured reddish-brown, and is used for making expensive furniture and other smaller articles, especially bowls. The Common Yew is best raised from seed; the cultivated varieties are propagated by cuttings or grafting.

The Japanese Yew, *Taxus cuspidata*, a native of eastern Asia, differs from the Common Yew in having abruptly pointed leaves, and is more resistant to frost. An even higher resistance is exhibited by the Canadian Yew or Ground Hemlock, *T. canadensis*, a low (3 to 7 ft), often straggling shrub which occurs in North America from Newfoundland to Vancouver and to Iowa. Its leaves are similar in shape to those of the Japanese Yew, but are arranged in two flat ranks, not two irregular V-shaped ranks as in that species. Both are cultivated in Europe, the Canadian Yew less frequently than the Japanese Yew.

California Nutmeg

Torreya californica

Trees of the genus *Torreya* are low-growing evergreens with large, flat needles and fleshy drupe-like fruits, found in the warm regions of North America and eastern Asia.

The species most often cultivated in Europe is the California Nutmeg *Torreya californica*, a native of the mountain valleys of California. It attains a height of 30 to 50 ft and has a long, broad, conical crown. The bark is greyish-brown tinged with orange. The glossy, dark green leaves are $1^1/_4$ to $2^1/_2$ in. long and about $1^1/_2$ in. wide, terminating in a sharp point. There are two grey bands of stomata on the underside. The flowers are inconspicuous, of two kinds, male and female, growing on separate trees and appearing in May and June. The female flowers produce in the autumn of the second year fleshy red-tinged fruits about $1\ ^1/_2$ in. long. The fruit consists of a bony-coated seed surrounded by a thin fleshy aril.

The California Nutmeg is a shade-living, slow-growing tree usually found in warm, moist coastal areas. It has very high quality wood, but in Europe it is cultivated only as an ornamental plant because of its slow growth and because it attains only small dimensions.

The closely related Japanese Kaya *T. nucifera* is a native of Japan; its leaves are linear, about one inch long, and the fruit is narrower and more elongate.

With their flat, pointed needles, the trees of the genus *Torreya* bear some resemblance to the Monkey Puzzle *Araucaria araucana*. The leaves of this tree are not arranged in two ranks but in a thick spiral, and the fruit is a cone about 4 in. long which disintegrates when ripe. It grows in the mountains between Chile and Argentina and attains a height of 130 to 160 ft. In Europe it is sometimes cultivated in parks in warmer regions with mild winters. It was introduced in Britain in 1795, and is commonly seen in suburban gardens.

European Silver Fir

Abies alba

The Silver Fir is an evergreen tree growing on the hills and mountains of central Europe, extending to the Pyrenees and the mountains of northern Spain, southern Italy, Macedonia and eastern Poland. It was introduced into England about the beginning of the 17th century.

A large tree, some specimens in the virgin forests of central Europe reach heights of up to 105 ft and are more than five hundred years old. It derives its name from the smooth silver-grey bark which it retains to an advanced age. The leaves are flattened needles, $^3/_4$ to 1 $^1/_4$ in. long, bluntly notched at the tip, green above, with two whitish bands of stomata below, arranged in two opposite ranks on the twigs. The dull crimson male flowers are clustered in catkins on the underside of the previous season's shoots. The female flowers, which form small greenish cones, are carried on the upper branches of the crown. The mature cones are reddish-brown, large and cylindrical (4 to 8 in. long and 1 to 2 in. wide), and stand erect on the branches; they mature at the end of September and when they disintegrate, the winged seeds fall to the ground. The European Silver Fir grows well in shade and is a typical forest tree, being a social individual and rarely standing alone. It is susceptible to severe frosts and requires moist soil and air. It is not well suited for planting in city parks. The wood is soft and light and is used in building underwater piles, ships, etc.

The Silver Fir, with its non-resinous buds and in its shape, bears a close resemblance to the Nordmann Fir *A. nordmanniana*, which, however, differs from it in having darker green leaves not arranged in two opposite rows. This tree occurs in the western Caucasus and northern Anatolia, at altitudes of 2600 to 6500 ft; it grows in similar situations to the European Silver Fir but is better suited for planting in parks. More resistant to drought and heat is the Greek Fir *A. cephalonica*, a native of the mountains of Greece, characterized by its sharply pointed needles.

The Asian firs most frequently cultivated in Europe are the Nikko Fir *A. homolepis*, which has rough bark and furrowed twigs, and Veitch's Silver Fir *A. veitchii*, which has soft leaves, dark green above, conspicuously white beneath, and was introduced into Britain in 1879.

Noble Fir

Abies procera

The genus *Abies* is represented in America by a large number of evergreen species, some of which are also widely cultivated in Europe. One of these is the Noble Fir, a native of the mountains in the states of Oregon and Washington, where it attains a height of 160 to 230 ft and develops a thick crown; at an advanced age it sheds its lower branches. The furry twigs are reddish-brown, and the buds are small and resinous. One of its most characteristic features is the shape and arrangement of the leaves on the twigs. They are the longest ($^3/_4$ to $1^1/_2$ in.) in the central part of the shoot, pressed close to the upper surface of the twigs at their bases, then curved sharply upwards. The leaves are blue-green, in the variety *glauca* almost silvery. The cones are large (up to 10 in. long and 3 in. in diameter) and attractive. The bracts are yellowish, very long and almost completely covering the dark grey scales of the cone.

The Noble Fir was introduced into Europe in 1830 and today is widely cultivated in parks in the western and central regions of the continent. In some countries (Britain, France and Germany), it is also grown in forest stands where it has proved to be a fast-growing species. It is propagated by seed, and requires an abundance of moisture and light.

Other American firs widely cultivated in Europe are the Giant Fir *A. grandis*, Colorado White Fir *A. concolor* and Balsam Fir *A. balsamea*. The Giant Fir is a native of California, extending north to Canada. It attains a height of more than 190 ft and is readily distinguished by the long ($^3/_4$ to 2 in.), two-ranked needles, resinous buds and rather small cones without marked bracts. The White Fir is an ornamental tree with blue-green to silvery sickle-shaped leaves $1^1/_2$ to 3 in. long. The cones are 3 to 5 in. long, without well-marked bracts. It is a native of western North America, extending from Colorado to northern Mexico. The Balsam Fir grows in the northern regions of North America and is distinguished by a narrow crown with a slender spire-like tip, and by smooth bark with raised resin blisters.

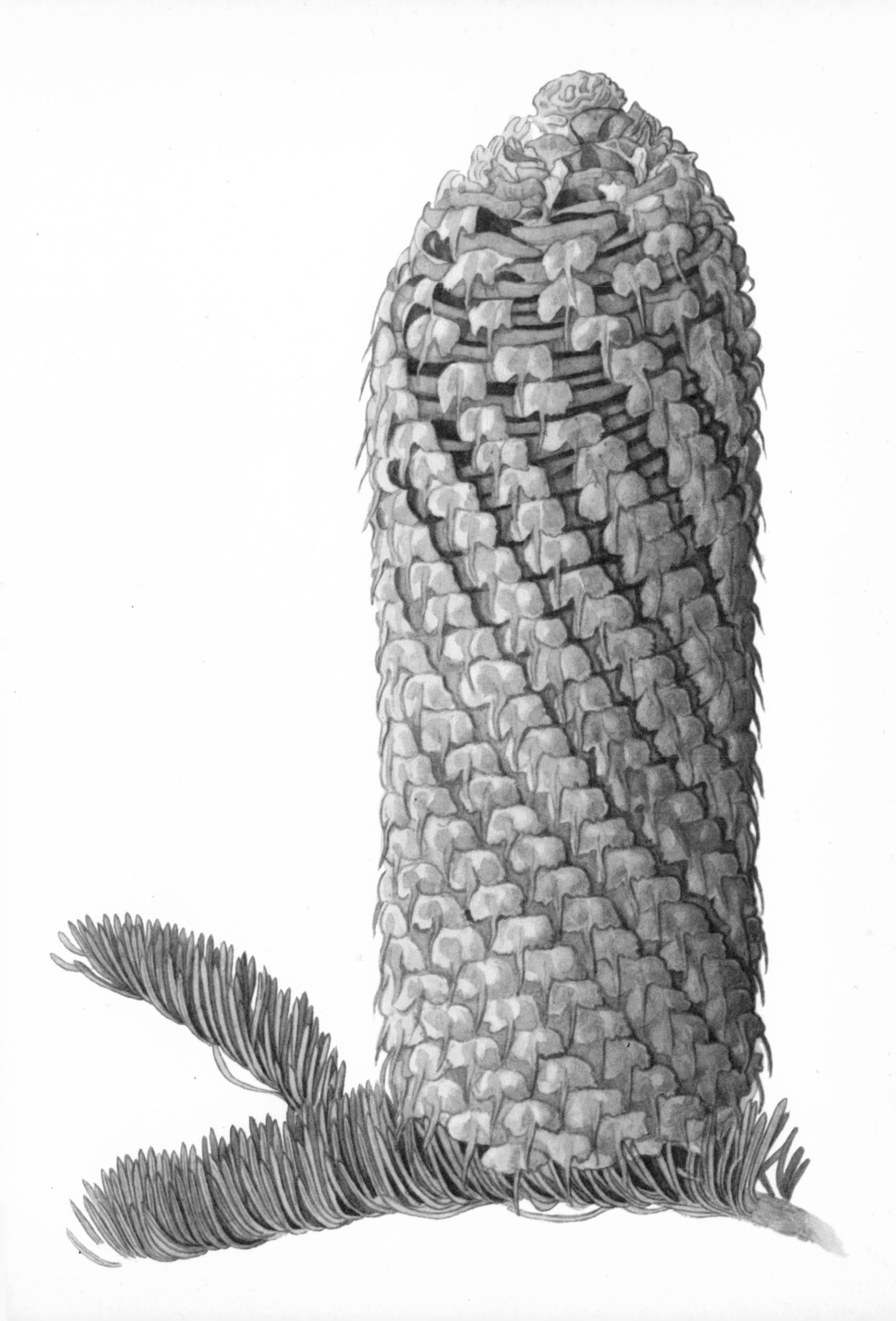

Common or Norway Spruce

Picea abies

The Norway Spruce is one of the largest evergreen trees of the mountain and lowland forests of central and northern Europe. In favourable situations it reaches 160 ft in height and has a narrow, conical crown with the branches arranged in regular whorls. The leaves are 1/2 to 1 in. long, rhomboid in section, with bluntly pointed tips and two to three lines of stomata on each side. They are borne on peg-like projections and are arranged in a spiral. Both the male and female flowers blossom in late April or May; the male flowers, yellowish in colour, are clustered in catkins on the previous season's shoots; the red cones of the female flowers stand erect at first, but after fertilization they turn green or purple and gradually becoming hanging. The mature cones are reddish-brown, cylindrical, 3 to 6 in. long. The winged seeds are shed from the cones on sunny days in spring. The root system is shallow and widespread, and the tree is often uprooted by strong winds. It grows best in shade or partial shade and requires abundant soil and atmospheric moisture. Strongly resistant to frosts, its range in Europe extends to the polar regions, and to altitudes up to the tree line. The soft, flexible wood is processed for a wide number of purposes both by mechanical and chemical means. The bark yields tannin and young specimens are used as Christmas trees.

Other Eurasian spruces, which are also widely cultivated in parks, are the Serbian Spruce *P. omorika* and Oriental Spruce *P. orientalis*. The Serbian Spruce, which is restricted today to a small area in central Yugoslavia, reaches a height of 130 ft and is distinguished by a slender crown, obtuse or bluntly pointed leaves, dark green above, with two broad white bands of stomata beneath, and small ovoid cones. The Oriental Spruce, a native of the Caucasus and north-east Turkey, has very short blunt leaves (1/6 to 1/3 in.) and narrow spindle-shaped cones.

Of the American species, the most widely cultivated in Europe is the Sitka Spruce *P. sitchensis* and the Colorado or Blue Spruce *P. pungens*. The Sitka Spruce is native to the coastal areas of western North America from Alaska to California; it was introduced in Britain in 1831. The leaves are narrow and sharp-pointed, the cones cylindric-oblong 2 1/2 to 3 in. long, with thin papery scales. The Colorado Spruce, a native of the Rocky Mountains, reaches a height of 100 ft, its leaves are stout, rigid, sharp-pointed, quadrangular in section with stomata on all four sides. The varieties with steel-blue to silvery needles are very popular in Europe as ornamental trees.

Douglas Fir

Pseudotsuga menziesii

The Douglas Fir, a native of western North America, is one of the tallest evergreen conifers, reaching a height of more than 260 ft. On old trees the bark is dark red-brown, thick and corky. The buds are sharp-pointed and shiny reddish-brown; the leaves are soft, green, flattened, 1/2 to 1 1/2 in. long, tapering towards the tip, with two greenish-white rows of stomata beneath. The ovoid cones are 2 to 4 in. long, with three-lobed, exserted bracts. The Douglas Fir begins to produce cones after the twentieth year. The form occurring in the Rocky Mountains is considered by some authorities as a separate species, *Pseudotsuga glauca*. It differs from the coastal form by its thinner and less deeply furrowed bark, blue-green foliage and cones with three-lobed strongly reflexed bracts.

The Douglas Fir is one of the most important timber trees of North America. The timber is not only produced in large quantities but is also of very high quality. The coastal form grows on a wide stretch of territory from California to British Columbia. It is a tree which prefers partial shade and is adapted to a long vegetation period and to withstand mild frosts. Open situations exposed to the wind are not suitable, nor are dry shallow soils. The Douglas Fir was introduced into Europe in 1828 and because of its rapid growth is now being widely cultivated in the forest stands of western and central Europe. It is propagated by seed.

The Rocky Mountain form occurs at altitudes above 6500 ft between latitudes 32° and 40° North. It is more frost-resistant than the coastal form and does not need as much soil nor such a high level of atmospheric moisture. Its growth is much slower and it does not attain such a great height.

Eastern or Canadian Hemlock

Tsuga canadensis

The Canadian Hemlock, a medium-sized evergreen tree about 100 ft high has a broad pyramidal crown composed of thin branches with pendulous tips. The buds are ovoid. The needles are flattened, comparatively short ($^1/_4$ to $^1/_2$ in.), tapering towards the tip and arranged in two opposite rows on the twigs. They are dark green above with two broad greyish bands of stomata beneath. The male and female flowers appear at the end of April, the latter after fertilization producing small ovoid cones 1/2 to 1 in. long. The small yellowish winged seeds are shed in the autumn and early winter.

The Canadian Hemlock covers a wide range in eastern North America, extending from Georgia to Canada (latitude 50° North), where it grows in mixed forests. It thrives on the cool moist soils near rivers and streams or on shady northern slopes; dry, warm situations are not particularly suitable for it. It was introduced into Europe in 1736; in western and central Europe it is cultivated as an ornamental tree in parks. It grows very slowly but is resistant to frost.

The Western Hemlock *Tsuga heterophylla* is more common in cultivation in the countries of western Europe with mild winters. It is a native of the moist coastal region of western North America, where it grows from California to Alaska. It attains a greater height than the Canadian Hemlock, and has a rapid growth rate. The buds are globose. The whitish bands of stomata on the underside of the needles are much broader than in the Eastern species and the seed scales of the cones are very long. It was introduced into Europe in 1851 and is being widely cultivated in western Europe, in forest stands, where it gives abundant yields. The wood is pale yellow-brown, fairly strong, and the bark is rich in tannin. In central Europe the Western Hemlock suffers from severe frost.

The Mountain Hemlock *T. mertensiana* is an attractive ornamental tree which attains a height of only 50 to 65 ft. It is a native of mountain districts in western North America, where it is found even at altitudes of more than 8000 ft. The needles are rounded or slightly keeled above, with stomata on both sides, and the cones are cylindric-oblong, 1$^1/_2$ to 3 in. long.

European Larch

Larix decidua

The larches belong to one of the few genera of deciduous conifers. They have horizontal branches and pale green linear leaves, which are arranged spirally on long shoots and densely clustered on short spur shoots. The European Larch is a native of central Europe, widespread in the mountains and hills of the Alps and West Carpathians. It is a pyramidal tree up to 130 ft high, with a dark greyish-brown bark and yellowish twigs. The needles are $^1/_2$ to $1\,^1/_4$ in. long, flattened, keeled, with two greenish bands of stomata, turning yellow when they fall. It flowers early in spring, at the beginning of April, when the leafless twigs are covered with red or green female and yellow male flowers. The erect cones, which are ovoid, $^1/_2$ to $1\,^1/_4$ in. long, remain on the tree for several years. The cone-scales are straight at the tip and softly hairy. Seeds are produced after the tenth to fifteenth year.

The most important forest trees are the ecotypes occurring in hilly districts of Czechoslovakia and Poland. They are cultivated throughout most of Europe. The European Larch, one of the most important forest conifers, grows vigorously and requires abundant light and air. It is particularly attractive in spring with its vivid light green foliage. This species was introduced in Britain before 1629.

The wood is of high quality, the heartwood reddish-brown and very durable; it is used chiefly in boat-building.

Very similar to the above is the Japanese Larch *L. leptolepis*, which reaches a height of 100 ft and has a more rapid growth when young. Its bark is thinner, and first-year twigs and cone-scales are bronze-coloured; the leaves have two white bands of stomata beneath, and the cone-scales are recurved at the tip. It occurs in the mountains of Japan and was introduced into Europe after 1860. This species exhibits particularly good growth in localities with a coastal climate, where it is being used also in forest plantings. The Dunkeld Larch *L. eurolepis*, is a hybrid between the European and Japanese Larches. It has been widely cultivated as a forest tree because of its vigour and resistance to diseases. Of the American species, one of the most commonly cultivated in Europe is the Tamarack or Eastern Larch *L. laricina*. Here it is usually not more than 65 ft high; it is distinguished by thin needles, small cones about half an inch long, and glabrous cone-scales.

Golden Larch

Pseudolarix amabilis

The Golden Larch is the only species of the genus *Pseudolarix*. It is a native of the eastern provinces of China, where it grows at altitudes of 1900 to 4500 ft above sea level. In its native habitats it attains a height of 130 ft, but in Europe it is not more than 65 ft tall. The trunk is branched from about the middle, and the branches are horizontal, forming a broad-conical crown. The bark is reddish-brown, fissured into narrow scales. The leaves are deciduous, linear, 1 to 3 in. long and up to 1/8 in. wide, soft, pale green, bluish beneath; they are arranged spirally and scattered on long shoots, forming clusters of fifteen to thirty leaves on short spur shoots which are longer than in the European Larch. When viewed against the sky from below, the branches and needles on the spur shoots form a characteristic and very decorative pattern. Before falling in the autumn the leaves turn a lovely golden colour. The flowers are monoecious, the male flowers catkin-like, the female flowers solitary. The cones are green at first, later turning yellow, 1 1/2 to 3 in. long, ovoid, with sharp-pointed, ovate-lanceolate scales arranged in the form of a rosette, separating from the axis at maturity. The Golden Larch was introduced into Europe in 1858 and grows well in both the western and central part of the continent. It requires abundant light and in dryer regions needs moist situations. It is highly valued as an ornamental tree but is not suited for forest cultivation because of its slow growth.

Cedar of Lebanon

Cedrus libani

Cedars are robust evergreen conifers, widespread along the shores of the Mediterranean and in the region of the Himalayas. The best-known is the Cedar of Lebanon, which was used by the Phoenicians to build their ships. It was also used in the construction of the Temple of Solomon in Jerusalem and for numerous other purposes by all the peoples of this territory, from the Egyptians to the Venetians.

The Cedar of Lebanon is a picturesque evergreen tree, 100 to 130 ft high, with a trunk 10 ft across. Mature trees are characterized by a broad, umbrella-shaped crown. The bark is dark grey, fissured and scaly in old trees. The leaves are needle-like, dark green, $^1/_2$ to $1\,^1/_2$ in. long; they grow scattered on the long shoots arranged in clusters of thirty to forty on short spur shoots. The flowers are monoecious; the male and female flowers, both resembling short yellow candles, appear in September. The cones are produced in winter. They are ovoid, 3 to 4 in. long, and grow upright on the twigs. In spring they disintegrate on the tree and shed the winged seed.

The Cedar of Lebanon grows in the Lebanon and in the Taurus and Antitaurus mountains in the eastern Mediterranean. Despite its southern origin it is quite hardy. In its native habitat it grows at altitudes of 4200 to 6500 ft above sea level, where it is exposed to temperatures of —22 °F (—30 °C) and for several months in winter is covered with a blanket of snow. In Europe the Cedar of Lebanon has been cultivated for more than three hundred years and huge specimens are found in the parks and gardens of England, France and central Europe. It is a sun-loving tree which requires a warm summer and moist sea air for best growth.

Also cultivated in Europe, though less commonly, is the Atlantic Cedar *C. atlantica*, which grows in stands in the mountains of Algeria and Morocco. It requires more warmth than the Cedar of Lebanon and differs also in having short pubescent twigs, shorter leaves and smaller cones.

The Deodar *C. deodara* is a native of Afghanistan and the northwest Himalayas, where it grows in mixed forests in mountain sides from 6500 to 8800 ft. It grows up to 95 ft or more, with a trunk about 10 ft in diameter. Its needles are about 2 in. long—almost twice as long as those of the Atlantic Cedar. The shoots and twigs are pendent and densely hairy. It has been cultivated in Europe since 1831, but is rather susceptible to frost.

Scots Pine

Pinus sylvestris

The Scots Pine is the dominant evergreen tree of northern Europe growing on poor soils, and the only pine which is native to Britain. It is very adaptable, both as to climate and soil, and grows in large forest stands from the Arctic to northern Germany and Poland. In southern Europe it is a mountain species.

The Scots Pine grows to 100 to 115 ft, and has an erect trunk and spreading branches, pyramidal when young, round-topped and irregular later. The bark is a reddish or greyish-brown, rather thick and fissured on the lower part of the trunk, copper-coloured on the upper part. The deep root system provides a firm anchorage and permits the tree to grow even on steep sandstone slopes and cliffs. The needles are $1^1/_2$ to 3 in. long, stiff, usually twisted and grow in pairs. The flowers are monoecious, the female flowers are in small reddish cones on the new shoots; the male flowers are in small globose yellowish catkins on the previous year's growth. The cones are short-stalked, reflexed, 1 to $2^1/_2$ in. long, covered with woody scales, and ripen in the autumn of the second year. The winged seed is carried great distances and produces many seedlings, especially in sandy situations and poor soils where this conifer is an important pioneer. The Scots Pine is a sun-loving, rapid-growing tree which thrives even in poorer and drier soils and is resistant to frost. It yields light, good quality wood, the heartwood pale brown, the sapwood a pale colour. The Scots Pine is generally regarded as a native in a few forests in Scotland, and is frequently planted and naturalized elsewhere in Britain.

Of the other European pines with leaves sheathed in pairs, one of the most widely cultivated is the Austrian Pine *P. nigra*, a native of southern Europe. It, too, attains a height of more than 100 ft and differs from the Scots Pine in having dark grey furrowed bark and longer (3 to 6 in.) dark green needles and larger cones. In central and western Europe it is used in the afforestation of karst, poor soils and sandy sea dunes. The Austrian Pine and its forms from Calabria, Corsica and Sicily, called the Corsican Pine subsp. *laricio*, are widely cultivated in Britain.

The Stone Pine *P. pinea*, a native of the Mediterranean region and Portugal, has an umbrella-shaped crown, a characteristic feature of the coastal landscape in that area. This tree may have been grown in Britain before 1548, and thrives reasonably well in the Midlands and southern England, in Wales and in Ireland. It prefers moist sandy soils and dislikes the presence of lime.

Two American pines, both with leaves mostly in pairs, are cultivated in Europe as ornamental or timber trees: the Jack Pine *P. banksiana*, a native of eastern North America, has cones $^3/_4$ to 2 in. long, long-conical, yellowish and very curved; the Lodgepole Pine *P. contorta*, is characterized by strongly twisted leaves and asymmetrical ovoid-conical brownish-yellow cones, $^3/_4$ to $2^1/_2$ in. long.

Weymouth or Eastern White Pine

Pinus strobus

Pines with leaves in groups of five are widespread in America, Europe and Asia, occurring not only in the temperate zone but also in the subtropics.

The best known of the American species is the Weymouth Pine. In its native habitat it attains a height of over 160 ft and is topped by an irregularly shaped crown of broad-spreading branches. The bark is greyish-green, smooth on young trees, becoming brown, rough and fissured on old trees. The needles are slender, flexible, $2^1/_2$ to 5 in. long. The cones are 3 to 6 in. long, pendent, cylindrical, often curved near the tip. They mature in the second season, shedding the seeds immediately after they ripen, and thus have to be picked as early as the beginning of September.

The Weymouth Pine is a native of eastern and central North America, from latitudes 40° to 50° North, where it grows on moist sandy loams or soils with a certain amount of clay. It was introduced into Britain in 1705 by the Duchess of Beaufort and Lord Weymouth and today is widely cultivated throughout western, central and eastern Europe for timber or as an ornamental tree. It is resistant to frost and because of its rapid rate of growth is cultivated also in forest stands in central Europe. It requires moderate light and has proved excellent in the improvement of poor, degraded soils. Its greatest enemy is the disease caused by the fungus *Cronartium ribicolum*, whose spread is greatly contributed to by the shrubs of the genus *Ribes*. Old, mature trees yield good quality heartwood which is used for various purposes. In Britain it has failed as a timber tree, but some old specimens are found in woods.

Indigenous to Europe are the Arolla or Swiss Stone Pine *P. cembra* and Macedonian Pine *P. peuce*. The first is a high mountain species growing near the tree line in the Alps and Carpathians. The cones are purplish-brown, broadly ovoid, $2^1/_2$ to 3 in. long, and do not open when mature. The seed, the size of a small nut, is wingless and edible. The Macedonian Pine is a native of the mountains of the Balkan peninsula. It is characterized by having a dense narrow-pyramidal habit and slow growth. Its cones are 3 to 6 in. long, nearly cylindrical, and the seeds are winged.

Of the Asian species with leaves in groups of five, the one most commonly cultivated in Europe is the Himalayan Pine *P. wallichiana*, a native of the temperate Himalayas. It has slender, pendent needles, 4 to 7 in. long, and cylindrical, curved, pale brown cones 6 to 10 in. long. It is a handsome ornamental tree, which keeps its large lower branches when old. In central Europe it is greatly damaged by frost in severe winters. It was introduced into Britain in 1823.

Italian Cypress

Cupressus sempervirens

The Italian Cypress, which is a native of the Aegean region, is a typical tree of the Mediterranean lands. It occurs in two forms: *pyramidalis*, with a narrow, cylindrical crown, and *horizontalis*, with a broad, spreading crown. It attains a height of 80 to 100 ft and has small, scale-like evergreen needles pressed close to the twigs. The seed is borne as early as in the fifth year. The globose cones, which mature at the end of the second season, are 1 to 1 1/2 in. long, yellowish-grey and composed of eight to fourteen abruptly pointed scales. The minute seeds have narrow lateral wings and retain the ability to germinate for up to ten years.

The Italian Cypress has a large, cylindrical root which penetrates deep into the ground and enables it to grow even in very dry situations. In the Mediterranean region it is used as a pioneer tree in the afforestation of karst or as an ornamental tree, and is often planted in cemeteries; the Romans associated it with death. In western Europe it is found only in coastal areas with mild winters; the climate of central Europe is not at all suitable to its growth. The wood is of very high quality and was used in ancient times for the building of temples and ships.

The attractive Monterey Cypress *C. macrocarpa*, a native of southern California, has ascending branches which form a broad to umbrella-shaped crown. In its native habitats it attains a height of more than 130 ft. The globose or ellipsoid cones are 1 to 1 1/2 in. long. It differs from the Italian Cypress in having larger leaves, smaller male flowers (less than 1/4 in.) and brown cones. For good growth it requires moist sea air and moist, aerated soil. In Europe it is planted as an ornamental tree only in the coastal countries.

Lawson Cypress

Chamaecyparis lawsoniana

Members of the genus *Chamaecyparis* are natives of America and Asia. They resemble the true Cypresses *(Cupressus)*, but have flattened twigs. In Europe the best known of the American species is the Lawson Cypress, often known in America as the Port Orford Cedar. It reaches a height of 130 to 160 ft and has a narrow, conical crown with pendulous terminal shoots. The needles are small and scale-like with narrow white markings beneath. The male flowers are purplish-red, the female flowers greenish. The globose cones, about $^1/_4$ in. long, mature in the autumn of the first season, shedding the small, winged seed at this time. The Lawson Cypress, which is indigenous in the mountain valleys of California and Oregon, growing alongside streams, was introduced in Britain through Messrs. Lawson in 1854 and today is widely cultivated in western and central Europe. Young trees grow well in shade, older ones require more light. This species prefers aerated, moist soils. It is very variable, and a large number of garden forms are known. The wood is very durable, exceptionally resistant to decay, particularly well suited for joinery and boat-building.

Other commonly cultivated North American species are the Nootka Cypress *Ch. nootkatensis* and the Atlantic White Cedar *Ch. thyoides*. The Nootka Cypress is distinguished by its drooping branches, dull green, glandular leaves without white markings and large cones, 3 to 4 in. long. It is restricted to the Pacific coastal area, from southern Alaska to southern Oregon. The Atlantic White Cedar has very slender branches and small cones (about $^1/_5$ in.) with scales terminating in a reflexed boss. It grows along the coast from Florida northward, in cold swamps and wet depressions.

The Sawara Cypress *Ch. pisifera* and Hinoki Cypress *Ch. obtusa* are natives of Japan. They are cultivated in central Europe only as ornamental trees but are highly valued as timber trees in their native country. Many horticultural varieties are known. The Sawara Cypress has acute obscurely glandular leaves with white markings beneath. The leaves in the Hinoki Cypress are obtuse, minutely glandular, with white X- or Y-shaped markings beneath.

The genus *Chamaecyparis* is closely related to the genus *Thuja*, the members of which are distributed in North America and Asia. They have larger leaves and oblong or conical cones. Of the North American species, the following are widely cultivated in Europe: the American Arbor-vitae *Th. occidentalis*, with yellowish or bluish-green glandular leaves without white markings beneath (introduced in 1596), and the Western or Giant Arbor-vitae *Th. plicata*, with dark green, nearly glandless leaves, with faint white markings below (introduced in 1853). The Chinese or Oriental Arbor-vitae *Th. orientalis* is a native of China, which differs from the American species in having usually several basal branches as long as the main trunk, entirely green leaves and wingless seeds. It is grown in Europe mainly for ornament.

Wellingtonia or Giant Sequoia

Sequoiadendron giganteum

The Wellingtonia is one of the evergreen trees famous for its huge size and remarkable length of life. Today the 'Big Tree' is found in about thirty isolated groves in the Sierra Nevada Mountains of California, where it grows on morainic soil in deep valleys. The massive old trees attain a height of 325 ft or more and are about 30 ft across. Their age is estimated at about 1500 to 3000 years. The reddish-brown bark, more than 20 in. thick on old trunks, is deeply fissured. The needles are short, bluish green, spirally arranged, appressed, with forward-pointing tips. The ovoid cones are 2 to 3 in. long; they ripen at the end of the second season. The seeds are small, flattened and laterally broadly winged. The Wellingtonia was introduced in Britain in 1853 and is now also planted in the parks of western and central Europe. It does well in a mild, coastal climate; in central Europe it suffers severely from frost. Sheltered situations on moist soil are best suited to its growth. The wood is highly prized for its durability.

The Redwood *Sequoia sempervirens* is a native of the coastal area of California and Oregon where it may grow up to 325 ft in height. It differs from Wellingtonia in having flat needles ($^1/_4$ to 1 in. long) arranged in two ranks and smaller cones ($^3/_4$ to 1 in. long). This tree can be cultivated only in southern Europe or in the coastal areas of western Europe where winters are very mild. It was introduced in Britain in about 1845.

Closely related to the Redwood is the Common Swamp or Bald Cypress *Taxodium distichum*. It is a deciduous tree 100 to 130 ft tall and more than 10 ft in diameter. The flat, $^1/_2$ to $^3/_4$ in. needles are borne on deciduous short shoots in two ranks. The globose cones, about an inch long, disintegrate when they fall from the tree. The Common Swamp Cypress is a native of the south-eastern United States where it grows in swamps. It was introduced in Britain in about 1640. This tree is ornamental and thrives well in moist soil or in ponds. In southern Europe it is planted for timber, especially on alluvial ground.

White Poplar

Populus alba

The genus *Populus* comprises numerous deciduous species classified in several groups, including the white poplars, black poplars and balsam poplars. They are dioecious species, the male and female flowers appearing on separate trees.

The best known of the first group is the White Poplar, which grows in stands alongside large rivers, from the Rhine to the Volga. In central Europe it attains a height of more than 100 ft, in England, where it is believed to have been introduced, only about 65 ft. It has a wide, spreading crown and a thick trunk covered at the base with black bark. The summer leaves (especially of the suckers) are palmately five-lobed, white and downy beneath. The flowers appear in March, the seeds being shed from the capsules in June. The root system is massive, the lateral roots extending far from the trunk and often producing root suckers. The White Poplar requires light and ample moisture and stands up well to regular spring floods. The wood is soft and not of great value.

The group of white poplars includes also the Aspen *P. tremula*. Unlike the White Poplar, it is a forest tree widespread throughout the whole of Europe, extending beyond the Arctic Circle in the north and growing also at high altitudes. The leaves are orbicular, the margin coarsely toothed. The leaf stalk is flattened laterally and consequently the slightest breeze sets the leaf in motion. The Aspen is a colonist tree and does not require rich soil.

Of far greater commercial value are the black poplars. The Black or Lombardy Poplar *P. nigra*, a native of south, central and eastern Europe, grows on river banks and wet woods, reaching a height of over 100 ft. The leaves are 2 to 4 in. long, rhombic-ovate to deltoid-ovate, with acuminate apex and without glands at the base of the blade. This species is often planted elsewhere and sometimes naturalized.

A poplar which is commonly cultivated in Europe today is a hybrid between the Lombardy Poplar and the Northern Cottonwood *P. deltoides* known as the Carolina Poplar *P. canadensis*. It is distinguished by rapid growth and is grown in plantations in short rotations of ten to twenty years. Several forms are known in cultivation, of which *serotina* is the commonest in Britain. Its branches are ascending and curve upwards, and the leaves often have one or two glands at the base of the blade. The female plant is unknown.

Of the balsam poplars the most widely cultivated in Europe are: the Balm of Gilead *P. gileadensis*, of unknown origin, perhaps a hybrid between the Balsam Poplar *P. balsamifera* and the Northern Cottonwood, both natives of North America; and the Western Balsam Poplar or Black Cottonwood *P. trichocarpa*, a native of Pacific North America from Alaska and British Columbia to California. Both have very sticky buds, with a strong balsam smell. In the Balm of Gilead the leaves are deltoid-ovate, pointed, usually heart-shaped at the base. The leaves of the Western Balsam Poplar are truncate or nearly heart-shaped at the base.

White Willow

Salix alba

The genus *Salix* comprises a large number of species widespread throughout the world. Most are deciduous shrubs or trees. In many cases their identification is very difficult, because most of the European species interbreed and produce fertile offspring which may re-cross or back-cross.

The White Willow is a tree up to 80 ft high, widely distributed in most of Europe except the Arctic, and eastwards to central Asia. It is also found in North Africa. It grows by rivers and streams, or on moist loamy ground. It can survive prolonged floods and in places where these are of a regular occurrence it is better suited than the Black Poplar. The leaves are lanceolate, 3 to 4 in. long, with finely toothed margin, and silky and hairy beneath. It is a dioecious species with flowers arranged in catkins which appear with the leaves; the male flowers are yellow, the female green. The small downy seeds are shed from the capsules in June. Propagation is easier by cuttings than by seed. The soft, light and flexible wood is used to make boats, charcoal and cellulose. Several varieties are found in cultivation, e.g. the Cricket-bat Willow, var. *coerulea*, quick-growing, leaves less hairy, cultivated for the manufacture of cricket-bats, mainly in southern England, var. *vitellina*, with bright yellow or orange twigs.

A closely related species is the Weeping Willow *S. babylonica*, a very picturesque tree with drooping slender branches often planted on borders of pools, in parks and gardens. It is regarded as an Asiatic plant; most of the 'Weeping Willows' in cultivation are hybrids between the Weeping Willow and the White Willow or Crack Willow. The Crack Willow *S. fragilis* is a tree up to 80 ft high, with a usually short and stout trunk and brittle twigs at the junctions. The lanceolate leaves are up to 6 in. long and are glabrous at maturity. It is found in much the same situations as the White Willow but occurs at higher altitudes and farther north. The Almond-leaved Willow *S. triandra* is a much-branched shrub or small tree, up to 32 ft high; its male flowers have three stamens.

Some tall shrubby species, with narrow leaves and stalkless catkins appearing before the leaves are called osiers. They grow by rivers and streams and in marshy places, and are cultivated to provide slender flexible shoots used in basket-making. The Common Osier *S. viminalis*, a shrub 10 to 16 ft high, has lanceolate or linear-lanceolate leaves, dark green and glabrous above, silvery silky-hairy beneath. It is widespread in central Europe, extending westwards to Ireland, northwards to England (in Scotland doubtfully native) and southern Scandinavia, eastwards to the Ukrainian Carpathians and Bulgaria. The Purple Osier *S. purpurea*, a shrub 7 to 10 ft high, has oblong-obovate to oblanceolate-linear, usually not quite opposite, smooth leaves, dull and slightly bluish-green above. It is found in most of Europe, except Finland and Scandinavia, Asia and North Africa.

The Great Sallow or Goat Willow *S. caprea* is a shrub or small tree, found in abundance in forest clearings, thickets and by lake shores. It reaches a height of 10 to 32 ft and has broadly ovate wrinkled leaves, downy beneath. The catkins are large and oblong-ovoid, about 1 to 2 in. long; they appear in March, well in advance of leaves. This species is widely distributed throughout all of Europe, extending far into Asia and occurring at altitudes above three thousand feet. It is of importance in forests as a common colonist.

Common Walnut

Juglans regia

The genus *Juglans* comprises several species which are of commercial value both for their fruit and wood. The best known in Europe is the Common Walnut. The centre of its natural range is in Central Asia. It extends westwards to southern Europe and the Balkan peninsula, eastwards to the Himalayas and China. It was widely cultivated by the Romans and the boundary of its distribution was extended northwards. It is commonly planted chiefly in southern and central Europe, France and West Germany; in Britain it has been cultivated from very early times. It attains a height of 65 to 80 ft; open grown trees have a short trunk and spreading crown. The pith of its twig is chambered as in all walnuts. The leaves are deciduous, odd-pinnate, composed of five to nine ovate leaflets with entire margins. The monoecious flowers (the male as hanging catkins, the female as terminal catkins) appear in May. The fruits are subglobose green drupes and appear in autumn; the green fleshy husk splits to release a hard wrinkled stone or nut which encloses a sweet, very tasty, oily, nutritious seed. The Common Walnut is a light- and warmth-loving species and does well on warm slopes, especially on fertile calcareous soils. In severe winters it suffers badly from frost. The high-quality heartwood is used primarily for furniture-making.

Of North American species, the Black Walnut *J. nigra* and Butternut *J. cinerea* are widely cultivated in Europe. The first is of far greater value as a timber tree. It attains a height of 100 to 130 ft. The odd-pinnate leaves are composed of thirteen to twenty-three leaflets with serrate margins; the nuts have a very thick 'shell', enclosing the seed. The Black Walnut grows in forests along the large rivers of eastern North America. It requires abundant light and does best on aerated moist soils of alluvial origin. The fruit is processed for its oil and the high-quality wood is used for making furniture and veneers. The Butternut is less commonly cultivated in Europe. It has ovoid, sticky-hairy fruits which hang in clusters, and the wood is of poorer quality.

Shagbark Hickory

Carya ovata

The genus *Carya* is closely allied to *Juglans* and comprises about twenty species, most of which are found in North America. Most commonly grown in Europe is the Shagbark Hickory, introduced to this continent at the beginning of the seventeenth century. It attains a height of more than 100 ft and develops an ovate crown. In winter it is conspicuous for its grey bark peeling off in long strips and large, alternately arranged buds. The leaves are deciduous, odd-pinnately compound, 8 to 14 in. long, comprising, as a rule, five ovate leaflets with serrate margins. The flowers are very similar to those of walnuts. The green drupes are subglobose, 1 to 1 1/2 in. long; the fleshy husk splits into four valves releasing a whitish, smooth, slightly four-angled nut containing a sweet, oily seed.

The Shagbark Hickory occurs in the broad-leaved forests of the lowlands of eastern North America. It requires cool, moist and comparatively rich soil. In addition to its edible fruit, it is also valued for its hard, flexible wood used to make skis, sleds, tool handles, etc.

The Mockernut Hickory *C. tomentosa* and the Big Shellbark Hickory *C. laciniosa* differ from the Shagbark Hickory in having leaves of seven to nine leaflets and thick-shelled nuts. The Mockernut is distinguished from Big Shellbark Hickory in having downy twigs and leaf-stalks and a husk not separating to the base. In the latter, leaf-stalks are often persistent during winter. The Bitternut *C. cordiformis* and the Pignut *C. glabra* have smaller fruits; in the former they are 1 to 1 1/2 in. long, four-winged, with a grey nut; in the Pignut the fruits are an inch long, slightly winged near the apex, with a pale brown nut. All four are also natives of eastern North America.

The hickories are closely related to the genus *Pterocarya*. Most common in cultivation in Europe is the Caucasian Wingnut *P. fraxinifolia* with a distributional range from Caucasus to northern Iran. The leaves are odd-pinnately compound, comprising eleven to twenty pairs of leaflets; the winged nuts hang in clusters.

Silver Birch

Betula pendula

The birches are broad-leaved deciduous trees of the Northern Hemisphere, the various species scattered throughout Europe, America and Asia. Most common in the Old World is the Silver Birch *Betula pendula* extending from Italy and the Balkan peninsula northwards beyond the Arctic Circle and eastwards into Siberia. It attains a height of more than 50 ft and develops a slender trunk terminating in a crown of slender, pendent branches. The bark is silvery white with black markings, smooth, peeling, becoming black and fissured towards the base of the trunk. The twigs are glabrous, covered with waxy warts and the leaves are deltoid to triangular, 1 1/2 to 2 1/2 in. long, with double-serrate margins. The male and female catkins appear with the opening of the leaves in April; the fruit—a small nutlet with two membranous wings—matures in July and August and is disseminated by the wind, sometimes as far as several miles. This explains the fact that the Silver Birch was an important colonist which occupied rapidly the areas left by the retreating ice sheet. It is a very tolerant tree, which is affected neither by frost nor by the sun's heat, grows well even on poor mineral soils and improves the situation, preparing the way for other trees. It is an ornamental element in the landscape, and its wood is widely used for many purposes including fuel.

The Silver Birch is closely related to the Common Birch *B. pubescens*, widely distributed on poor acid, especially peaty, soils of moorland and mountains throughout northern and central Europe, northwards to 71° North and southwards to central Spain and Yugoslavia. It is distinguished from the Silver Birch by its downy twigs and leaves.

American species frequently cultivated in European parks include the Canoe Birch *B. papyrifera*, Cherry Birch *B. lenta*, Yellow Birch *B. lutea* and River Birch *B. nigra*. The first is distinguished by thick, chalk-white bark, impervious to water, used by the American Indians to build their canoes. The Cherry Birch and Yellow Birch have oblong-ovate leaves similar to those of the Hornbeam. The bark of the former is black, that of the latter brownish-yellow. The River Birch, growing in the swamps and along the stream banks of the United States, has deltoid leaves and blackish bark which peels off from the trunk in strips.

Common Alder

Alnus glutinosa

Alders are deciduous trees which usually grow on moist sites and are found along watercourses and by lakes, pools and marshes. The Common Alder *Alnus glutinosa* is widespread in most of Europe, extending from Spain and Italy northwards to Norway and Sweden and eastwards to Siberia. It reaches a height of 65 to 100 ft and develops a straight trunk with an oblong crown. The bark is dark sooty-brown. The Common Alder is easily recognized in winter by the ovoid, stalked buds. The broad leaves have a truncate to notched apex and are sticky in spring. The flowers are monoecious, the male and female flowers arranged in catkins, appearing early in spring before the leaves open. After fertilization, the scales of the female catkins become hard and green, persisting and becoming black after the small winged fruits have fallen out. The fruits have buoyant corky outgrowths and may be carried by water for great distances. The Common Alder is marked by vigorous propagation by stump sprouts, and is often cultivated in copses. Attached to the roots are nitrogen-fixing nodules which serve to increase the nitrogen content of the soil. The Common Alder is a sun-loving, fast-growing tree, forming stands in the valleys of rivers and streams or in swampy or wet situations. The soft orange-coloured wood is used for foundations of bridges, plywood, matches and pencils.

The Grey Alder *A. incana* is a native of northern Europe and the mountains of central Europe, differing from the Common Alder by the smooth pale grey bark and pointed, ovate leaves. In northern forests it is of importance in reforestation and improvement. The American species, the Smooth Alder *A. rugosa,* is a shrub or a small tree up to 32 ft high, distinguished by ovate leaves with a wedge-shaped base, and red-brown hairs at least in the axils of veins. It is frequently planted and naturalized, mainly in central Europe.

Common Hornbeam

Carpinus betulus

The genus *Carpinus* comprises about fifty species found in eastern Asia, Europe and North America. The Common Hornbeam is a tree up to 80 ft high, with a fluted trunk covered with smooth grey-green bark. The leaves are deciduous, elliptical to ovate, $2^1/_2$ to $4^1/_2$ in. long, with a doubly serrate margin and a pointed apex. The male and female catkins appear during April and May. The fruits are small, ovoid, ribbed nuts, subtended by a large three-lobed involucre which makes wind dispersal possible. The seed germinates in the spring of the second year. The Common Hornbeam is widespread in central and south-east Europe, extending to southern Italy, western France, south-east England, southern Sweden and White Russia, where it occurs in woods, sometimes as a coppiced shrub in oak-woods. It grows well in shade and is moderate in its demands on soil properties and moisture. The decomposing leaves serve to enrich the soil. Its vigorous regenerations by stump sprouts and its thick crown make it highly valued in landscape architecture, being used for hedges and decorative plantings. The wood is tough and close-grained, well adapted for the tool trade and excellent as fuel. The American Hornbeam *C. caroliniana*, a native of eastern North America, is cultivated occasionally in European parks. It attains a height of about 30 ft and differs from the European species in having leaves with more pointed tips.

Closely allied to *Carpinus* is the genus *Ostrya*, comprising only four species found in Europe, North America and Japan. The European Hop-hornbeam *O. carpinifolia*, a native of southern Europe and Asia Minor, and the American Hop-hornbeam *O. virginiana*, a native of North America, resemble the Common Hornbeam in the shape of the crown and leaves, but the fruits, ribbed nutlets, are enclosed by a bladder-like involucre. In the European Hop-hornbeam the leaves are usually rounded at the base, with glandless leaf-stalks and ovoid nutlets. The leaves of the American Hop-hornbeam are usually nearly heart-shaped at the base, with stalked glands, and the nutlets are spindle-shaped. In western and central Europe they can be cultivated only in regions with a warm climate.

Common or European Beech

Fagus sylvatica

The Common Beech is an important timber tree as well as a handsome ornamental plant. It attains a height of 100 to 130 ft and develops a long, smooth silver-grey trunk terminated by a broad rounded crown. Open-grown specimens have a wide crown reaching almost to the ground. The buds are brown, long and pointed. The leaves are deciduous, ovate, 2 to 4 $^1/_2$ in. long, the margins entire to slightly serrate. The young leaves are pale yellowish-green, becoming darker with age. In the autumn the leaves turn reddish or golden brown. The flowers of both sexes appear on the same tree after the opening of the leaves. The fruits are three-angled, dark reddish-brown and glossy, enclosed in a woody four-lobed prickly husk. Heavy crops appear at intervals of from five to eight years. The ripe nuts are shed at the end of September and are a favourite food of forest animals. In times past pigs were herded into beech stands to fatten on the nuts. The Common Beech prefers a coastal climate and does not extend far to the east; in southern Europe it occurs in mountains, and to the north it is found in Britain and in the southern part of Sweden. It grows well in shade, often in pure stands, but also in mixed stands with conifers and other broad-leaved trees. The beech is a highly valued forest tree because of its rich natural propagation by seed, its few insect pests, and because the fallen leaves keep the soil rich and in good condition. The hard wood is used in the making of furniture, parquet flooring and cellulose. It is popular as an ornamental tree in parks, where it is represented by several varieties characterized by drooping branches, bronze-purple leaves and columnar trunks.

The American Beech *F. grandifolia*, a native of North America, is sometimes planted in European parks. Its leaves are sharply serrate, elongate and thickly veined; they, too, are brightly coloured in the autumn.

Sweet Chestnut

Castanea sativa

The genus *Castanea* is of great commercial value not only for its wood and tannin but also for its edible fruit. It comprises about fourteen species found in North America, Europe and eastern Asia. The Sweet Chestnut *C. sativa* is a native of southern Europe, extending eastwards from Italy to Iran and northwards to Hungary. The Romans, however, introduced it in many other parts of Europe and today centuries-old trees may be found in Britain and central Europe. The Sweet Chestnut is a deciduous tree, up to 100 ft high, with a trunk over 6 ft thick. The leaves are ornamental, oblong-elliptical, 5 to 8 in. long, sharply serrate. The male and female flowers, borne on long upright catkins, appear in June. The fruits are large, brown, leathery nuts, one to three together enclosed in a green, spiny involucre or cupule, which in autumn splits into two to four lobes. Roasted nuts are a favourite delicacy in winter. The Sweet Chestnut is extensively planted for the nuts and timber and is naturalized in many parts of western, central and northern Europe. It requires partial shade but is a warmth-loving tree, so that outside its natural range it is cultivated only in warm and sheltered areas. The high-quality durable wood is used to make barrels, furniture and also for its tannin.

The American Chestnut *C. dentata*, which is a native of North America, resembles the Sweet Chestnut, but its leaves are glabrous beneath, the winter buds are glabrous or nearly so, and the nuts pointed at the apex. It was highly valued as a timber and fruit tree, but at the end of the nineteenth century it was exterminated in many areas by the fungus *Endothia parasitica* brought here from China.

The most highly valued of the Asian species is the Japanese Chestnut *C. crenata*, which is also cultivated in many varieties. It requires plenty of soil and atmospheric moisture and therefore thrives best in coastal areas. Today this species and the Chinese Chestnut *C. mollissima* are being hybridized with the American and European species to produce disease-resistant trees.

Turkey Oak

Quercus cerris

The genus *Quercus* comprises many species distributed throughout the whole world, except Australia. The best known and most common in Europe are the Common Oak *Q. robur* and the Durmast Oak *Q. petraea*. They are majestic trees, up to 130 to 140 ft high, with robust trunks and strong branches, attaining an age of five hundred to a thousand years. The leaves are deciduous, with five to eight pairs of rounded lobes. The male flowers are in pendent, thin catkins; the female flowers are grouped in clusters of two to five. The fruit is an elliptical acorn partially enclosed by a cupule. The Common Oak has sessile leaves and stalked fruit; the Durmast Oak has stalked leaves and sessile fruit. Both grow from southern Europe through central and western Europe to southern Sweden. *Q. robur* prevails on heavy soils in woods along watercourses, while *Q. petraea* is generally found on drier slopes and hillocks. The wood of the oak is highly valued and is used to make veneers, furniture, ships and barrels.

The Turkey Oak *Q. cerris*, a native of southern Europe and western Asia, is a fast-growing deciduous tree up to 110 ft tall. Its leaves are deeply lobed, with pointed lobes; the cupule enclosing the acorn, which ripens in the second year, is covered with spreading and reflexed linear, downy scales. In central Europe and England, where it was introduced in 1735, it is occasionally cultivated in parks, naturalized in some places. The Holm Oak *Q. ilex* is planted elsewhere in western and southern Europe, also in Britain, and rarely naturalized. The small elliptical leaves are evergreen, glossy green above, downy below. Its natural range is the Mediterranean region from Spain and North Africa to Asia Minor. It grows well in dry situations and is a very handsome tree, especially in winter.

Of the American species resembling European deciduous oaks, most frequently cultivated in Europe are the White Oak *Q. alba* and the Bur Oak *Q. macrocarpa*. The former has thin, scaly pale-grey bark and obovate to oblong-obovate leaves, with five to nine oblong and obtuse lobes, which turn red in the autumn. The Bur Oak has scaly, light brown, deeply furrowed bark, and obovate to oblong deeply lobed leaves, 4 to 12 in. long, which turn yellow-brown in the autumn.

Red Oak

Quercus rubra

The Red Oak, a native of North America (from Canada southwards to Virginia and Kansas), is the most important species of the red oak group. It is a robust deciduous tree reaching a height of over 110 ft and when grown in the open develops a broad crown with strong branches. The bark remains smooth grey-green to an advanced age. The leaves, 4 to 10 in. long, have pointed lobes and turn scarlet in the autumn. The acorn is long, subglobose, enclosed in a shallow flat cup; it matures in the second season. The Red Oak grows more rapidly when young than the European oaks and has a higher yield of wood. It does not require particularly rich soil and grows also on acid soils. For these reasons and because of its rapid growth it is sometimes planted in central Europe in forest stands. It is also a popular ornamental tree. The timber is heavy, with red-brown heartwood, and is used for the same purposes as European oak, although its quality is not as good.

Other North American red oaks cultivated in Europe are the Pin Oak *Q. palustris* and Scarlet Oak *Q. coccinea.* Both attain a height of 65 to 80 ft and are distinguished by their drooping branches. The leaves are 3 to 6 in. long and deeply lobed. The acorns in both species are half the size of those of the Red Oak; they also ripen in the second season. The Pin Oak, which grows in moist and swampy situations, has leaves with conspicuous axillary tufts of hairs beneath, and its acorns are about one-third enclosed by a thin saucer-shaped cup with hairy scales. The Scarlet Oak does well also on light, drier soils. Its leaves have small axillary tufts of hairs beneath and the acorns are enclosed about one-third to one-half by a hemispherical cup with nearly glabrous scales. Its handsome bright green foliage turns brilliant scarlet in autumn. The Black Oak *Q. velutina*, another native of North America, is cultivated locally in western Europe. Its lobed leaves, 5 to 8 in. long, are hairy beneath; the acorns are long, ovoid, up to half enclosed in a deep cup.

Wych Elm

Ulmus glabra

Elms are large deciduous trees which often dominate landscapes, especially near rivers. The leaves are asymmetrical—one half of the blade is larger than the other and set lower on the stalk. The most important of the European species is the Wych Elm *Ulmus glabra* which attains a height of 100 ft and develops a dome-like crown with ascending branches. Young shoots are thickly covered by short hairs. The leaves are obovate, 3 to 6 in. long, terminating in a sharp point at the tip. The flowers are hermaphrodite, appearing in early spring before the leaves. The fruits, orbicular samaras with membranous wings, ripen in May. The range extends from southern Europe north to central Scandinavia; it is found high up in the mountains and is most plentiful by streams, in moist ravines and on stone debris with rich soil. It is a tree requiring partial shade and is marked by rich natural reproduction from seed. The wood, medium-heavy with brown heartwood, is used in making furniture, veneers and parquet flooring.

Other European representatives of this genus are the Smooth Elm *U. minor* and European White Elm *U. laevis*. Both are widespread mainly on alluvial deposits where they occur in mixed stands with the Common Oak, Common Alder and Black Poplar. The European White Elm is distinguished by its trunk suckers, glabrous leaves and long-stalked, haired fruit. The Smooth Elm has small leaves and short-stalked fruit with a seed close to the closed notch. Besides growing in forests and open country, elms are also found in parks where they are cultivated as ornamental trees, especially their hybrids. One of the North American species sometimes grown in Europe is the White Elm *U. americana* which generally resembles the European White Elm, but differs from it in having leaves widest about the middle, often nearly glabrous beneath.

Closely related to the elms are *Zelkova carpinifolia*, a deciduous tree native to the Caucasus and Iran, which is characterized by having partly unisexual flowers, wingless fruits and simply serrate leaves; and the Hackberry *Celtis occidentalis*, a deciduous tree native to North America, which has unisexual flowers, leaves acuminate at the tip and a fruit in the form of an orange-red to dark purple drupe.

White Mulberry

Morus alba

The White Mulberry is always thought of in connection with the silkworm and the production of silk. It is a native of China, introduced and naturalized in other parts of Asia, in America and in southern Europe. Its leaves serve primarily as food for the silkworm *Bombyx mori*, which spins a large cocoon of silk fibres. The production of rayon and man-made fibres has somewhat lessened the importance of silk, but the silkworm is still widely cultivated in many countries of Asia and Europe.

The White Mulberry attains a height of 30 to 50 ft. The leaves are deciduous, broadly ovate, often irregularly notched, almost glabrous beneath. The small unisexual flowers are clustered in short separate catkins. In summer after fertilization the female flowers produce fleshy, white to pinkish aggregate fruit which is edible. This mulberry grows in the mountain forests from Asia Minor to China. In Europe it is sometimes cultivated in parks as a solitary tree, in warmer regions also in tree avenues, and is well suited for planting as hedges. In central and western Europe it suffers markedly from frost during more severe winters. This tree does not thrive well in Britain. The Black Mulberry *M. nigra* is a central Asiatic tree, with leaves hairy beneath and a dark purple aggregate fruit. It is widely cultivated for its fruit and locally naturalized in southern Europe. The Red Mulberry *M. rubra*, a native of North America, is a large tree attaining a height of 80 to 100 ft, the leaves truncate or slightly cordate at the base, softly hairy beneath, and the aggregate fruit is coloured dark red. In Europe it is cultivated less frequently than the two Asiatic species.

Closely allied to the mulberries is the Osage-orange *Maclura pomifera*, a low deciduous tree up to 50 ft high, with dense, ovoid crown and spiny twigs. The pointed leaves are entire, ovate to oblong-lanceolate. The aggregate fruit is spherical, of the size of an orange, golden-yellow, consisting of drupelets. The Osage-orange is a native of the southern United States and is cultivated in Europe as an ornamental tree or as a hedge in the warmer regions, naturalized in southern Europe. It is less frequently planted in parks than the Paper Mulberry *Broussonetia papyrifera*, which is a native of Japan and Korea and has ovate or three-lobed leaves measuring 3 to 8 in. and an orange-coloured aggregate fruit about an inch in diameter.

Soulange Magnolia

Magnolia × soulangiana

Magnolias, natives of North America and eastern Asia, are in evolutionary terms the oldest of the broad-leaved trees; they are also one of the most ornamental groups. They are distinguished by large elongate leaves and large solitary flowers with numerous spirally arranged stamens and carpels and a cone-like fruit from which the mature seeds protrude. Most commonly cultivated in Europe is the Soulange Magnolia *Magnolia × soulangiana*, a fertile hybrid of the Chinese species *M. denudata* and *M. liliflora*, distinguished by its pubescent buds, large ovate leaves and rose-white flowers about 4 in. long. The flowers appear early in spring before the leaves unfold. The forms of this hybrid are more frequently planted than the parental species. The most popular species in England is the Laurel Magnolia or Bull Bay *M. grandiflora.* The leaves are evergreen, elliptical, 5 to 8 in. long, and the large, cup-shaped flowers measure 6 to 8 in. in diameter. It is native to the south-eastern United States, where it reaches a height of more than 65 ft. One of the first magnolias to be introduced into Europe (in 1688) was the Sweet Bay *M. virginiana.* It has fairly small deciduous leaves, 3 to 5 in. long and white, cup-shaped flowers 2 to 3 in. in diameter. Another North American species is the Umbrella Magnolia *M. tripetala*, a deciduous tree with leaves 10 to 24 in. long, standing upright near the ends of the branches like the ribs of an umbrella. The creamy-white flowers measure 5 to 10 in. in diameter and have heavy odour. The largest of the North American magnolias is the Cucumber Tree *M. acuminata*, an important forest tree, up to 100 ft high; the leaves are elliptical, 5 to 8 in. long; the flowers, greenish, 2 1/2 to 3 in. long, do not appear till June. It is frost-resistant.

Of the Asian species, the most commonly cultivated in Europe are *M. stellata* and *M. denudata.* The first is a Japanese evergreen shrub or small tree with white star-like flowers composed of narrow petals which appear in early spring. The second species, a native of central China, is an evergreen tree with white, bell-shaped flowers.

Tulip Tree

Liriodendron tulipifera

The Tulip Tree has an ancient history. Fossil remains indicate that before the Ice Age it was widely distributed in Europe. It is a large tree attaining in Europe a height of 80 to 100 ft and developing a straight trunk with roughly furrowed bark. In winter it is distinguished by the peculiar buds shaped like a duck's bill. The leaves are ornamental, conspicuous and very distinctive. They are 5 to 6 in. long, saddle-shaped, with two to four lateral lobes, broadly notched at the tip. The flowers are tulip-shaped. The petals are yellowish-green with orange spots at the base; the stamens and pistils are numerous. The fruit is brown, cone-like, each carpel consisting of a one to two-seeded nutlet with a long narrow wing; it ripens in autumn.

The Tulip Tree grows in the eastern United States from Florida northwards, chiefly in river valleys on fertile, alluvial soils. The wood, with yellow heartwood and pale sapwood, is light and used to make veneers, musical instruments, etc. It is a warmth-loving species, but also does well in sheltered situations in central and western Europe where it is cultivated for ornament for its unusual flowers and leaves and the yellow colour of its foliage in autumn.

China Tree

Koelreuteria paniculata

The China Tree, or Pride of India, is a very attractive species with its characteristic leaves. It is a deciduous tree up to 32 ft high and the trunk generally branches close to the ground so that it resembles a large shrub. The odd-pinnate leaves, sometimes bipinnate, are 8 to 18 in. long, composed of seven to fifteen ovate, lobed leaflets; they grow in clusters at the end of the twig. The yellow flowers are clustered in erect panicles; they appear in July. The fruits are capsules containing three blackish seeds. This tree, a native of China, Korea and Japan, is sensitive to low winter temperatures and can be cultivated in Europe only in regions with a mild climate. It does best on fertile soils.

The buckthorns are in a family related to the China Tree. The most common European buckthorns are the Alder Buckthorn *Rhamnus frangula* and Purging Buckthorn *Rhamnus cathartica*. The name of the former is derived from the Common Alder which is its associate on peaty ground at the margins of fens and bogs and in swampy habitats. It is a large deciduous shrub or small tree 5 to 22 ft high, with purplish-grey twigs with white lenticels. The alternate leaves are entire, obovate or elliptic, 1 to 3 in. long, turning yellow and dark red in autumn. The greenish-yellow flowers appear successively between May and July. The fruits are small berries, which turn from red to black. The Purging Buckthorn is a deciduous shrub or small tree 10 to 25 ft high. The branches terminate in strong thorns, the buds are scaly and the leaves are ovate, finely serrate, and opposite. The flowers are usually dioecious, the fruit a black berry with four seeds. These berries are strongly purgative. Both buckthorns are widely distributed in most of Europe, extending eastwards to western Asia, southwards to Morocco and Algeria.

London Plane

Platanus × hybrida

The London Plane is considered to be a natural hybrid between the Oriental Plane *Platanus orientalis* and the American Plane or Buttonwood *Pl. occidentalis*, originated at Oxford about 1670. The famous tree in the grounds of the Bishop's Palace at Ely is known to have been planted by Bishop Gunning between 1674 and 1684. It is much more adaptable and frost-resistant than the parental species and has thus become widely distributed throughout central Europe all the way to the Baltic Sea. It is a deciduous tree which attains a height of more than 100 ft and a trunk diameter of over 6 ft. In open situations it develops a broad, rounded crown with strong branches. The trunk is mottled as the bark peels off in large flakes exposing the yellowish inner bark. The five-lobed leaves are 6 to 8 in. long, with the width of the lobes about equal to their length. The male and female flowers are borne in separate pendulous, globose heads. The fruits are small achenes, clustered like the flowers in globose heads just over an inch in diameter, hanging in groups of two to three on long stalks. The London Plane sometimes produces fertile seed in Britain. It is a common shade or street tree and is planted as an ornamental tree in parks, for it does well in the smoke and dust-laden atmosphere of big cities. When the leaves expand, a rusty down is shed which floats in the air and may cause minor eye irritations.

The Oriental Plane is a native of the Balkan peninsula and the Near East. It attains an age of more than a thousand years and some specimens are known to have a diameter of more than 10 ft. The lobes of the leaves are deeply notched and the bark peels off in large flakes. There are two to six fruit-heads. It is sensitive to low temperatures but the climate of Great Britain is suitable to its growth.

The American Plane is a native of North America. Its leaves have shallow notches and the bark peels off in small flakes. It thrives in Britain, but is less commonly cultivated in Europe. It is frequently called the Sycamore.

Wild Pear

Pyrus communis

The Wild Pear has given rise to the numerous varieties cultivated today for their sweet, tasty fruit. It was originally native only to southern and central Europe and western Asia but has been cultivated by man since ancient times (it is common in the vicinity of human habitations) so that its range of distribution has become widespread. The Wild Pear is a small deciduous tree which reaches a height of 50 to 80 ft and develops a narrow, often pyramidal crown, with short, thorny branches. The bark is fissured in squares. The orbicular, finely serrate leaves are alternately arranged on the twigs on long stalks; the whitish flowers with red anthers appear in early May. The fruit is round to pear-shaped, yellow-green to yellow when ripe, 1 to 2 in. long. Unlike the apple, this tree requires a warmer climate and is therefore much less common in northerly countries.

The Wild Pear is seldom planted for ornament. Its relatives the Snow Pear *P. nivalis*, a native of southern Europe, and the Willow-leaved Pear *P. salicifolia*, a native of south-eastern Europe and western Asia, are cultivated in the parks of central Europe. The leaves in the former are linear-lanceolate to lanceolate, shining above, but in the latter they are elliptic to obovate.

Purple Crab

Malus × purpurea

The genus *Malus* comprises a great number of species, some of which provide numerous cultivated varieties which are common fruit trees in temperate Europe. Most species originated in central Asia, some are also native to south-east and central Europe, but it is difficult to find the precise boundaries of their original range which have been changed by man since ancient times.

The most important species, from which the majority of cultivated varieties are descended, are the Crab Apple *M. sylvestris* and the Wild Crab *M. pumila*. Both are small deciduous trees, 18 to 30 ft high. The Crab Apple has ovate, green leaves, pinkish flowers and yellow-green, round fruit; the leaves of the Wild Crab are tinged with pink, the flowers are pink to red, and the fruit elongate, yellow to purplish. Frequently planted in parks and gardens is var. *niedzwetzkyana*, an ornamental variety of this species.

This genus includes many handsome ornamental trees, which in spring are enveloped in a cloud of pink to dark purple flowers, and in autumn are bright with the yellow to red colours of their fruit. These ornamental garden species are generally hybrids cultivated chiefly from the Wild Crab and following Asiatic species: *M. halliana*, *M. prunifolia*, *M. sieboldii* and *M. floribunda*. Among the most beautiful ornamental plants is the Purple Crab *M. purpurea*, with its purple leaves, wine-red flowers and dark red fruit. It is a hybrid between *M. pumila* var. *niedzwetzkyana* and *M. × atrosanguinea*.

Whitebeam

Sorbus aria

Some members of the genus *Sorbus* bear little resemblance to the Mountain Ash and were formerly placed in other genera. An example is the Whitebeam which is a deciduous shrub or small tree up to 60 ft high. The broadly elliptical leaves are covered with white down beneath and have a serrate margin. The white flowers appear at the end of May. The fruits, almost spherical, fleshy, with a scarlet, often dotted skin, grow in clusters; the stalk and remainder of the calyx are covered with white down. The Whitebeam is found throughout southern, central and western Europe, in England and Sweden reaching the northernmost limit of its range. It is locally abundant, especially on chalky or limestone soils, in central Europe even at altitudes over 3000 ft. It grows on most well-drained soils, in country or town. The wood of this species is of little commercial value and it is cultivated chiefly as an ornamental tree.

Related to the Whitebeam is the Wild Service Tree *S. torminalis*, which has more or less the same range of distribution though it does not extend to Scandinavia. It is a warmth-loving species and it is not found at high altitudes in the mountains. The Wild Service Tree is a deciduous tree, reaching up to 65 ft in height. The bark on the trunk peels off in scales. The leaves are broadly oval, with six to ten deep triangular sharply toothed lobes, downy when young, becoming glabrous. The fruit is brown, ellipsoid, greenish-brown with small dots; it is eaten by birds. It is a slow-growing tree; the wood is heavy, hard and tough. Representing a link between the Whitebeam and Wild Service Tree is the Broad-leaved Whitebeam *S. latifolia*, which in its characteristics is intermediate between these species, and is considered to be a hybrid between them. It has broadly ovate to ovate leaves, pinnately lobed with short broad-triangular sharply serrate lobes. It is a native of southern Sweden, the Baltic States and north-eastern Germany. Its leaves are broadly elliptical, shallowly notched, covered with green down beneath. It is often planted as an ornamental tree, introduced in many other countries, sometimes sown by birds and freely naturalized.

Mountain Ash

Sorbus aucuparia

The Mountain Ash or Rowan is a deciduous tree attaining a height of 40 to 65 ft and an age of eighty to one hundred and twenty years. The bark is smooth and grey-brown. The alternate, odd-pinnately compound leaves, measuring 5 to 7 in. in length, comprise nine to fifteen lanceolate, sharply serrate leaflets. The white flowers grow in thick clusters; they appear in June and are succeeded in autumn by bright-red fleshy fruits the size of peas. The fruits are a favourite food of birds; the Latin name *aucuparia (avis capere)* indicates that they were used by bird-catchers to bait their traps. The Mountain Ash comprises also varieties with sweet fruit (var. *edulis*) cultivated in rugged northern or mountainous regions for their fruit, which is used to make compotes, jams and spirit.

The Mountain Ash is widespread throughout Europe; in the western and central part of the continent it occurs mainly in the mountains, in the north it extends beyond the Arctic Circle. It is resistant to frost and thrives even on poorer soils. It is of importance as a colonist which is distributed by birds and quickly covers burned and logged areas; it is also an ornamental species suitable for planting alongside roads.

The Service Tree *S. domestica* is very similar to the Mountain Ash but differs in having a rough, longitudinally fissured bark, leaves slightly downy beneath and pear-shaped fruits about an inch long. It grows wild in southern Europe, North Africa and western Asia. Also cultivated in Europe, though less frequently, is the American Mountain Ash *S. americana*, a native of North America, which resembles the Mountain Ash in its fruit, flowers and leaves, but differs in having sticky, glossy buds.

Midland Hawthorn

Crataegus oxyacanthoides

The genus *Crataegus*, which is distributed in the north temperate zone, comprises numerous species, about ninety in the Old World; several hundreds have been described from North America, but much reduced by recent authors. The Midland Hawthorn *C. oxyacanthoides* and the Common Hawthorn *C. monogyna* are the most common species in Europe. They are small deciduous trees up to 40 ft tall, often branching near the ground when young, thus resembling a shrub. As in most hawthorns, the twigs are spiny and the buds globose, reddish, with sinuses not reaching half-way to the midrib; there are normally two styles. The leaves of the Common Hawthorn are deeply cut with narrow lobes, with sinuses reaching more than half-way to midrib; there is one style. The snowy flowers expand in May, the solitary trees at this time resembling huge white bouquets. The fruits are bright crimson berries, known as haws, with two to three seeds in the Midland Hawthorn and only one in the Common Hawthorn. In forestry the Midland Hawthorn is valued as a colonist in the forestation of pastures but it is of far greater importance as an ornamental plant. It is also used for making hedges and tree avenues; the red or white-flowered varieties of this species are very attractive.

Of the North American species, the Cockspur Thorn *C. crus-galli* and the Dotted Thorn *C. punctata* are most frequently cultivated in Europe. They are distinguished from the species described above by their sharp thorns, 1 $^1/_2$ to 2 in. long, obovate leaves and $^1/_2$ in. globose, red berries, which in the Dotted Thorn are sparsely dotted. Of the numerous hybrids cultivated in gardens and parks, Lavallee's Thorn *C. lavallei* is the most popular. It is considered to be a hybrid between a Mexican Thorn *C. pubescens* and the Cockspur Thorn. Its leaves are deeply cut, shining green above, paler and very downy beneath, turning bronze-coloured in autumn.

The Common Firethorn *Pyracantha coccinea*, a native of southern Europe and western Asia, is a dense shrub or small tree, 6 to 12 ft tall, with thorny branches, small, persistent, elongate-ovate pointed leaves and bright red berries $^1/_4$ in. across.

Strawberry Tree

Arbutus unedo

The Strawberry Tree, a native of southern Europe (Mediterranean region to south-western France, and Ireland), is an erect shrub or small tree, up to 40 ft high. When introduced into more northerly regions it is generally of lesser height, often growing as a shrub. The leaves are evergreen, leathery, ovate to obovate, 2 to 4 in. long, glossy dark green above, with finely serrate margin. The bell-like cream-white or pinkish flowers are borne in broad drooping panicles and open in September, at the same time as the fruits of the previous year begin to ripen. The fruit is orange-red, globular, $^1/_2$ to $^3/_4$ in. across, resembling the strawberry. The surface is covered with numerous blunt tubercles. The Strawberry Tree is very attractive, especially in autumn, when, in addition to its dark green leaves, it is covered with white flowers and red berries. It will grow in almost any soil, both dry and acid, but is very sensitive to frost and thus in western Europe can be cultivated only in coastal regions.

It is closely related to the Madrona *A. menziesii*, which is a native of North America, growing in the coastal region from British Columbia to California. It is an evergreen tree up to 100 ft tall, which is valued for its timber. The leaves are longer and broader than these of the Strawberry Tree; the flowers grow in upright pyramidal panicles and the fruit is a little larger. It is rarely planted in Europe.

Gean or Wild Cherry

Prunus avium

The genus *Prunus* comprises many species and is of great economic importance, because it includes numerous fruit trees such as cherry, plum, apricot, peach, etc. The most widespread wild-growing tree in Europe is the Gean or Wild Cherry. It is difficult to determine the precise boundaries of its original range for it has been widely cultivated over the centuries and is found today in most of Europe from Scandanavia (64° North) and south-western Russia southwards, also in North Africa and western Asia. It occurs as a scattered tree in broad-leaved woods. It is a deciduous medium-sized tree 65 to 80 ft tall, with a long, smooth trunk covered with a reddish-brown bark. The ovate leaves, 2 $^1/_2$ to 5 in. long, are roughly serrate. The white flowers open in early May and are succeeded by the dark red fruit which ripens in July. The fruit is eaten by birds which disperse the seed throughout the surrounding countryside. The red-brown wood is of high quality and is used in making furniture and in joinery. A closely allied species is the Sour Cherry *P. cerasus* which is a small tree bearing sour fruit; its origin is unknown; propagation is frequently by root suckers.

Of Asian origin are the Apricot *P. armeniaca* and the Peach *P. persica*. The first has broad to ovate bluntly serrate leaves and white or pinkish flowers; the fruit is a yellow-orange drupe with a smooth flattened stone which separates easily from the flesh. The Peach has lanceolate, sharply serrate, long pointed leaves, 3 to 6 in. long, pinkish-red flowers and subglobose fruits covered with velvety down. Its stone is deeply pitted and grooved, and is not easily separated from the flesh. Both species require warm and sheltered situations.

A common shrub widespread in most of Europe, except the north-east and extreme north, is the Blackthorn or Sloe *P. spinosa* which forms thorny scrub on dry slopes and on the margins of forests. The white flowers appear before the leaves unfold; and the round, black-blue fruit measures about $^1/_2$ in. in diameter. Widely cultivated in the gardens and orchards of Europe is the Plum *P. domestica*, a related species, which includes a large number of cultivated forms.

Black Cherry

Prunus serotina

The Black Cherry is a medium-sized deciduous tree which grows to a height of 65 to 100 ft. The bark is dark brown. The oval to oblong-lanceolate pointed leaves are 2 to 5 in. long, leathery, lustrous green above, light green beneath and often downy along the midrib. In autumn they turn yellow. The whitish flowers grow in racemes; they appear in June, and are succeeded in September by black, globose fruit, eaten by birds which spread the seed great distances.

The Black Cherry grows in the wild in eastern North America from Texas to Ontario. It attains large dimensions only on fertile soils in valleys and on slopes, where it occurs together with other broad-leaved trees. It is a fast-growing species with moderate requirements of light and soil moisture. In Europe it is sometimes cultivated in parks or planted in tree avenues. It produces light, red-brown wood of good quality and the possibility of growing it in forest stands for timber is being studied in central Europe.

The Bird Cherry *P. padus* is a native of Europe growing throughout almost the entire continent and far to the north. It reaches a height of only 30 to 50 ft, growing in moist situations near rivers and brooks. The leaves are more sharply serrated than in the Sweet Cherry and the fruit is black, about $^1/_3$ in. wide, with a sour taste. It is eaten by birds.

The Mahaleb Cherry *P. mahaleb*, a native of southern Europe and south-western Asia, is related to the Black Cherry. It is a small deciduous tree, up to 30 ft tall. The leaves are orbicular to broadly ovate, 1 to 2 $^1/_2$ in. long, bluntly short-pointed, pubescent along the midrib beneath. The fruit is black, about $^1/_4$ in. across. The Mahaleb Cherry requires warm situations. Its wood is used for making pipes and cigarette-holders.

A handsome ornamental plant is the Cherry Laurel *P. laurocerasus*. It is a native of the Balkans and the Caucasus and occurs as a shrub or small tree with leathery, evergreen, oblong to obovate-lanceolate, distantly serrate leaves, 2 to 7 in. long.

Yellow-wood

Cladrastis lutea

The Yellow-wood is a small deciduous tree reaching a height of 30 to 65 ft with a broadly ovate crown. The buds stand upright on the twig in groups of three to four, one behind the other. In summer and autumn they are concealed by the leaf stalk. The leaves, 10 to 16 in. long, are composed of seven to eleven entire, ovate leaflets, and are arranged alternately on the twigs. The ornamental racemes of white flowers are 8 to 16 in. long, and appear at the end of May, succeeded in autumn by brownish pods 2 1/2 to 3 in. long, containing three to six seeds.

The Yellow-wood is a native of the United States in the mountain valleys of the Appalachians. It requires fertile moist soil and will grow in partial shade. Although an ornamental species, it is rarely seen in the parks of Europe.

Closely related to the Yellow-wood is *Maackia amurensis*, a tree up to 65 ft tall with a straight trunk and broad, ovate crown. The odd-pinnately compound leaves, consisting of seven to nine entire leaflets, are 4 to 12 in. long. The white flowers grow in thick, upright clusters; the flat, brown pods are only 1 1/2 to 2 1/2 in. long. It is a native of China and the eastern USSR, where it grows in mixed stands in river valleys. It does well in the shade but requires moist, fertile soil. The wood is of good quality and very durable.

Black Locust

Robinia pseudacacia

The Black Locust or False Acacia was given its Latin name after the French botanist Jean Robin, who introduced it into Europe in the seventeenth century. Its natural range is in eastern North America, chiefly Pennsylvania and Georgia. Today it is widespread in western, central and southern Europe and in some regions had become naturalized to such an extent that it is considered to be a native. It is a deciduous tree, up to 65 to 100 ft high. The bark is reddish-brown and deeply furrowed; the buds are scaleless and hidden by the leaf-stalk before leaf-fall. The ornamental odd-pinnately compound leaves consist of nine to seventeen elliptical leaflets with rounded apex. The leaves appear late in spring—at the end of May. The white, sweet-scented flowers, hanging down in dense clusters, provide a rich harvest for bees. The fruit is a flat brown pod, 3 to 4 1/2 in. wide. The Black Locust is a fast-growing species when young and will grow on poorer soils. Because of its widespreading root system and ability to develop numerous root suckers, it has been used in Europe for erosion control on slopes, embankments and sand dunes. The wood is very durable and of high quality and so the Black Locust has also been cultivated in Europe in forest stands. The trunk is straight only in warm situations where it is protected against early frosts.

Closely related to the Black Locust is Clammy Locust *R. viscosa*, also a native of North America, frequently grown in parks and gardens. It is a more ornamental species with sticky, glandular twigs without spines, and with pink flower clusters. It can be grown only in sheltered sites.

Common Laburnum

Laburnum anagyroides

The genus *Laburnum* comprises three smooth-barked, deciduous trees or shrubs, distinguished by their long-stalked leaves, each consisting of three short-stalked leaflets, and by their numerous flowers in long hanging racemes.

The most common species is the Common Laburnum or Golden-chain or Golden-rain *L. anagyroides*, a native of central and southern Europe, commonly cultivated in Britain and naturalized in some places. It is a large shrub or small tree, up to 30 ft high, with downy hairs on the twigs and pods, and on the underside of the leaf. Racemes of yellow flowers 12 in. long appear in May, and the bush in blossom looks as if it is covered with golden cascades, hence its popular name 'Golden-rain'. The fruit is a small pod 2 in. long, which persists on the tree till the following spring. All parts of the plant, from the leaves to the fruit, are poisonous; rodents, however, nibble the twigs and the bark without any harmful effects. Laburnum is a popular ornamental plant which does particularly well on chalky soils.

The Scotch Laburnum *L. alpinum* is closely allied to the Common Laburnum. It has glabrous twigs and leaves and racemes of flowers are up to 16 in. long. The flowers appear about three weeks later than on the Common Laburnum. Its natural range is the Alpine region from France to Austria.

A truly remarkable species is *Laburnocytisus adami*, a graft-hybrid or chimaera, which was developed in France by the grafting of the Purple Broom *Cytisus purpureus* on the stem of the Common Laburnum. In habit it resembles the Common Laburnum, but the leaflets are smaller and nearly glabrous. It bears reddish flowers, but also the red and yellow flowers of the parent stock.

Honey Locust

Gleditschia triacanthos

The Honey Locust acquired its Latin name after the botanist J. Gleditsch and its three-branched spines, which occur on the trunk and on older branches. It is a native of eastern North America, its range extending from Texas as far north as the 43rd parallel, where it is found in mixed stands of broad-leaved trees on moist soils. It is a deciduous tree, up to 100 ft high; the bark is smooth, nearly black, coming off in large scales. The three-branched spines are reddish-brown, 2 to 6 in. long. The leaves are both even-pinnate and bipinnately compound, 5 to 11 in. long, with sixteen to twenty-eight small leaflets. The small greenish flowers grow in clusters. The fruit is very ornamental and is characteristic of this tree; it is a red-brown, flat pod, 10 to 16 in. long and about an inch wide. The Honey Locust is a warmth-loving species which does best in the southern half of the European continent.

Closely related to the Honey Locust is the Judas Tree *Cercis siliquastrum*, a native of Southern Europe and western Asia. It is thought to be the tree on which Judas hanged himself. It is deciduous and attains a height of only 30 to 40 ft. The trunk is stout and twisted, generally branching low and forming a broad crown. It is distinguished by its bright pink flowers which appear in clusters on mature and leafless branches, and even on the trunk in spring before the leaves unfold. The glaucous green, entire alternate leaves, 3 1/2 to 5 in. wide, slightly less in length, are nearly orbicular, deeply heart-shaped at the base. The fruit is a flat pod. It does not do well in the colder climate of central and north-west Europe but is frequently planted as an ornamental tree in parks and tree avenues in southern Europe.

The closely allied Eastern Redbud *C. canadensis* is a smaller tree with smaller flowers. It is less sensitive to frost than the European species.

Tree of Heaven

Ailanthus altissima

The Tree of Heaven is a hardy deciduous tree attaining a height of 65 to 80 ft, with a stout trunk and smooth, dark grey, slightly fissured bark. The young shoots are stout and greenish. The odd-pinnately compound leaves, 12 to 24 in. long, consist of thirteen to forty-one stalked, ovate, pointed leaflets with one to four large glandular teeth near the base. The small greenish flowers are borne in panicles, the male and female usually on separate trees. The fruit consists of one to five winged samaras, each with a single central seed; the wing can take the seed great distances in windy weather.

The Tree of Heaven is a fast-growing, sun-loving tree which flourishes in light, aerated soil, requiring little soil moisture. It also does well in the smoky atmosphere of cities, and was widely planted in bombed and devastated towns and cities after the Second World War. A native of western China, it was introduced in 1751, and is now fairly common in the cities of central, western and southern Europe, as well as in America. A tree of southern origin, it is easily damaged by severe frosts and grows well in the warmer regions of central and western Europe. In China it sometimes serves as food for the silkworm.

Staghorn Sumach

Rhus typhina

The Staghorn Sumach, which was introduced in Europe from eastern North America several centuries ago, is the commonest European representative of the genus *Rhus*. It is a dioecious, deciduous shrub or small tree up to 30 ft tall, often forming groups which develop from root suckers. In winter it is easily distinguished by its stout, rusty-brown, velvety hairy branches and showy crimson fruit clusters, which remain on the tree until the following summer. The alternate, odd-pinnately compound leaves consist of eleven to thirty-one oblong-lanceolate, pointed, serrate leaflets. When they are plucked, droplets of milky juice ooze from the stalk. The leaves are very ornamental, and in autumn they change to vivid hues of orange, red and purple. The flowers are greenish and are borne in densely hairy clusters; the fruit is a small, crimson, densely hairy drupe.

The Staghorn Sumach is a sun-loving species which flourishes on poorer soils with a low moisture content. Because of its tendency to develop root suckers, it is sometimes planted on hillsides to prevent erosion. The leaves contain as much as twenty-five per cent tannin, and experiments are being carried out in some countries of Europe to cultivate it in plantations for this product. A related well-known producer of tannin is the Mediterranean species *R. coriaria*.

The Varnish Tree *R. verniciflua*, a native of China and Japan, yields a sap used for the production of Chinese lacquer. The leaves are entire and the fruit is a straw-yellow drupe. This plant is very poisonous.

Common or English Holly

Ilex aquifolium

The Common Holly is a slender evergreen shrub or small tree up to 60 ft in height, and attaining an age of one hundred years. The trunk is silver-grey. Its ornamental leaves are very characteristic. They are tough, leathery, ovate or elliptic, dark glossy green above, 1 to 3 in. long, and edged with spiny teeth. Sometimes the leaves are spineless, especially on the upper branches of mature trees. The spines and the structure of the leaves are a means of protecting the plant against frost and grazing cattle. The small whitish flowers appear in May and are borne in clusters in the axils of the leaves. The male and female flowers are produced on separate trees. The fruit is red, globose and fleshy, with one to six stones. They are eaten by birds which thus aid in spreading the plant.

The Common Holly is a native of western Europe, occurring in regions with a coastal climate as far north as Sweden. In central and eastern Europe it suffers badly from frost in severe winters, and is not found in countries with a typical continental climate. It will grow in almost any soil and thrive in shade. In parks and gardens it is planted not only in groups but also as hedges, because it can be clipped. There are numerous cultivated ornamental varieties.

The American Holly *I. opaca* is a larger species with solitary flowers or inflorescence in the axils of the leaves on young branchlets. It is rarely found in Europe in cultivation. In its native country, the United States, it is used for timber. Like the European species, it is a popular Christmas decoration.

Sycamore

Acer pseudoplatanus

The genus *Acer* comprises about one hundred and fifty species, mostly deciduous trees, found in the temperate Northern Hemisphere. It is distinguished by upright buds, palmately lobed leaves and long-winged double samaras.

Of the European species the most important is the Sycamore which attains a height of 100 to 115 ft and a diameter of over 6 ft; it can live to an age of several hundred years. It has yellow-green buds, five-lobed serrate leaves and greenish-yellow, scented flowers of both sexes growing in hanging panicles. The flowers expand shortly after the appearance of the leaves and are succeeded by clusters of fruits, consisting of two one-seeded samaras joined together with long, membranous, slightly spreading wings. The wood, light in colour and hard, is used to make furniture, veneers and musical instruments. The Sycamore is a native of the mountains in central and southern Europe but has been widely planted and naturalized in other parts of the continent. It seeks partial shade, is moderate in its requirements as to soil properties and moisture, and is sensitive to severe frosts. It was introduced in Britain about the 15th century. In America the name Sycamore is usually applied to the American Plane.

Another European species is the Norway Maple *A. platanoides*, also a large deciduous tree, which reaches a height of over 100 ft but not as great a diameter. It differs from the Sycamore in having red-violet buds, dark grey longitudinally fissured bark and five- to seven-lobed, sharply pointed leaves. The flowers appear before the leaves and the samaras have widely spreading wings. It is widespread in most of Europe, the extreme north, the extreme west and the islands. In the south it occurs only in mountains. It has been planted for ornament and occasionally naturalized in some places.

The Common Maple *A. campestre* is also a European species. It is widespread in most of Europe, from northern England, southern Sweden and central Russia southwards, but rare in the Mediterranean region. It is also planted for ornament. It is usually a small deciduous tree or shrub up to 50 ft high, and has small buds. It is generally found on dry hillsides in thickets and on the margins of forests. During the Napoleonic Wars, when England's blockade of Europe prevented the import of cane sugar, attempts were made to produce sugar from the sap of the maple. Despite a certain success, preference was given, however, to the cultivation of sugar-beet for this purpose.

Box-elder or Ash-leaved Maple

Acer negundo

The genus *Acer* is abundantly represented also on the American continent and in eastern Asia. The commonest of the North American species is the Box-elder, a small deciduous tree up to 65 ft high, attaining an age of one hundred years. The twigs are bluish-green, the leaves long-stalked, bright green, pinnate, with three to five ovate, slightly lobed leaflets; the flowers are dioecious, appearing at the end of April before the leaves unfold; the double samaras hang in long drooping clusters. Frequently planted in parks are the vividly coloured forms var. *variegatum* and var. *auratum*. The Box-elder has been cultivated chiefly for ornament. In Britain it was introduced in 1683.

The following North American species have been also cultivated in parks and gardens in Europe: the Silver Maple *A. saccharinum*, a medium-sized tree up to 100 ft high with five-lobed leaves with deeply and double serrate, pointed lobes, silver-grey beneath. It flowers about March, the fruits (samaras) maturing in June. It is a native of eastern North America and does best on moist, fertile soils. Similar in size is the Red Maple *A. rubrum*, which has three- to five-lobed leaves with red petioles and triangular-ovate, short-pointed, unequally serrate lobes, dark green and glossy above, usually hairy on the veins. Both the flowers and the winged samaras are red. It grows in moist to swampy situations. The Sugar Maple *A. saccharum* is valued in the United States and Canada not only for its high-quality wood but also for the maple sugar produced by boiling the sap. The leaves resemble those of the Norway Maple, but in the flowers the sepals are fused and petals absent.

East Asia is the original home of many species of maples with small ornamental leaves. The most frequently cultivated is the Japanese Maple *A. palmatum*, a native of Japan and Korea. The leaves are deeply five- to nine-lobed, purplish-red or golden yellow depending on the variety. It is a variable shrub or small tree 12 to 30 ft high. The leaves are deeply divided into five to nine serrate lobes. The flowers are purplish, and the wings of the fruit spread at an obtuse angle and are incurved above.

Common Horse Chestnut

Aesculus hippocastanum

When in flower the Common Horse Chestnut is one of the most attractive trees. It is a native of western Asia and south-east Europe, where it occurs in mixed mountain and broad-leaved forests. It is a stout deciduous tree attaining a height of over 80 ft and developing a dense, ovoid crown. In winter it is distinguished by its large, sticky, opposite buds and the twisted form of the trunk. The large, palmately compound leaves, comprising seven obovate leaflets, unfold in early spring. The flowers, borne in upright racemes, appear in May, making the Horse Chestnut look something like a lighted Christmas tree. The flowers are whitish with yellow and reddish-brown spots. In autumn they are succeeded by thorny, leathery capsules about 2 in. across, containing one or two brown nuts. These are often collected by children, and eaten by roe-deer and red-deer. The tree was introduced into central and western Europe in the sixteenth century and is often planted in avenues, parks and game preserves. It grows in partial shade and prefers rich, moist soil.

The genus *Aesculus* also has several representatives in America. The best known is the Red Buckeye *A. pavia*, which reaches a height of only 20 to 40 ft and differs from the Horse Chestnut in having non-sticky buds, leaves comprising only five leaflets, and clusters of red flowers. Frequently planted in the parks of Europe is the Red Horse Chestnut *A. carnea*, a hybrid between the Common Horse Chestnut and the Red Buckeye. The trunk, crown and leaves resemble those of the Common Horse Chestnut; the red flowers are like those of the Red Buckeye.

Less common in parks and gardens of Europe is the Sweet Buckeye *A. octandra* of North America. This species reaches a height of 50 to 65 ft and has palmate leaves of five serrate leaflets; the flowers are yellow.

Silver Lime

Tilia tomentosa

Limes or Lindens (*Tilia*) are long-lived deciduous trees whose magnificent stature made them honoured and highly valued in ancient times. The most widely distributed species is the Small-leaved Lime *T. cordata*, which grows throughout Europe. It attains a height of 100 to 115 ft and develops a long, straight trunk in forest stands and a short one with a broad ovate crown when it grows in the open. The leaves are heart-shaped, abruptly pointed, 1 to 2 in. long, green above, blue-green below, with tufts of rusty hairs in the axils of the veins. The Small-leaved Lime is a late-flowering species, the scented, yellowish blossoms not appearing till July. The tree is visited by bees and is thought to be important for honey production. The fruit is a globular nut, $^1/_6$ to $^1/_4$ in. across, not or obscurely ribbed, with a leafy bracteole on the stalk. The Small-leaved Lime is distributed throughout almost all of Europe, north as far as Sweden, Norway and Finland, and east as far as the Urals, also in the Crimea and Caucasus. It can attain an age of several hundred years. It is a very prolific sprouter and lends itself to clipping. The wood is soft and whitish, used chiefly for wood-carving.

Another European species is the Large-leaved Lime *T. platyphyllos*, which differs from the Small-leaved Lime in having red twigs, larger leaves, green above and hairy beneath, and hard, strong ribbed nuts. It flowers about two weeks earlier. It is doubtfully native in Britain. The Common Lime *T.* × *vulgaris*, a variable tree, widespread in most of Europe, also in Britain, and much planted, is intermediate in character between the Small-leaved and Large-leaved Limes, and is considered to be a hybrid between these species.

A tree which has been widely planted in the towns and cities of central and western Europe during the past few decades is the Silver Lime *T. tomentosa*, a native of south-eastern Europe, which does better in the dry and smoky atmosphere than other species and retains its leaves for a longer time. The leaves are silvery hairy beneath. The globular nuts are also downy.

Sometimes cultivated in the parks and gardens of Europe is the American Lime *T. americana*, an attractive tree up to 130 ft tall, with broadly ovate leaves, 4 to 8 in. long, abruptly pointed, light green beneath.

Flowering Dogwood

Cornus florida

The genus *Cornus* comprises about fifty species occurring in the Northern Hemisphere from America to eastern Asia. The majority are shrubs and only a few are tree-like forms. One of the most striking when in full bloom is the Flowering Dogwood, a native of eastern North America. It is a shrub or small tree, up to 35 ft high, which develops a broad, spherical crown. The twigs are green, the leaves opposite, ovate, abruptly pointed, and with arched veins. The flowers are small, greenish-white or yellowish, arranged in heads above four large white bracts resembling petals. When in flower (in June) the tree looks like one huge, white bouquet. The fruit is a red, ellipsoid drupe, 1/2 in. long, crowned with a persistent calyx. The Flowering Dogwood is sufficiently frost-resistant for the climate of central and western Europe, but occurs only infrequently there because of the difficulty of propagation.

The best known of the European species is the Red Dogwood *C. sanguinea*, a deciduous shrub only 10 to 16 ft high with bright red twigs. The white flowers appear in June. The fruit is a blue-black berry about 1/4 in. across. In the autumn the leaves turn red. It is found throughout almost all of Europe except in the north, growing most abundantly in lowland forests, at the edge of woods or in thickets on slopes. It grows well in shade and is resistant to frost. Its bright coloured forms are frequently cultivated in parks.

The Cornelian Cherry *C. mas*, a native of southern Europe, warm regions of central Europe and western Asia, is a tree-like shrub 13 to 20 ft high, which flowers in early spring before the leaves unfold. The yellow flowers are succeeded by scarlet berries 1/2 to 3/4 in. long, used to make marmalade and liqueurs. It is a warmth-loving species which prefers sunlight and does well even in dry situations. All dogwoods produce a very hard, heavy wood which is used to make various small articles.

Common Persimmon

Diospyros virginiana

Members of the genus *Diospyros* are mostly tropical or subtropical species yielding highly valued wood (ebony) or edible fruit. Of those which thrive in the temperate zone, one of those most often planted in Europe is the Common Persimmon. It is a native of eastern North America, growing in the Mississippi River basin where, under favourable conditions, it reaches a height of 65 to 100 ft. It was introduced into Europe at the beginning of the eighteenth century and is cultivated, though rarely, in England, France and Italy where it occurs as a small-sized tree only about 30 ft high. The alternate, oblong-ovate leaves, 2 to 3 in. long, turn golden brown in autumn. The whitish flowers, generally dioecious, grow in the axils of the leaves. The fruit is an edible, orange-red, 1-in. berry. Many varieties have been produced in the United States. The Common Persimmon thrives in sunny situations, both moist and dry; in central and western Europe it suffers from frost in severe winters.

Of the tropical species, True Ebony *D. ebenum*, a native of the dry monsoon forests of Ceylon, is known as a timber tree, producing very hard and durable black timber. The Chinese Persimmon *D. kaki*, a native of the mountains of central China, has long been cultivated in China and Japan for its fruit. Its globose or ovoid yellow-red fruit is 1 to 4 in. in diameter and its flesh resembles apricot jam in consistency, colour and flavour. Nowadays it is cultivated throughout the subtropical zone from America through Europe to Asia.

The persimmons are related to the Japanese Snowball *Styrax japonica*, a native of China and Japan, planted in sheltered situations in Britain and southern Europe as an ornamental plant for its pretty clusters of white flowers.

Indian Bean

Catalpa bignonioides

The genus *Catalpa* consists of ten species found in North America and eastern Asia. Commonest in European parks is the Indian Bean *C. bignonioides*, a broad-crowned deciduous tree, up to 65 ft high. The leaves are heart-shaped, 5 to 9 in. long, opposite or whorled, often in whorls of three, light green, with an unpleasant smell when crushed. The trio of buds and the swellings formed around the large scars left by the fallen leaves are very characteristic, allowing easy identification of the trees in winter. The Indian Bean in flower (July) is a showy ornamental plant with upright panicles of yellow-white flowers spotted brown and purple. The fruit is a long slender capsule, 6 to 12 in. long, which splits along two sutures to release the flat fringed seeds inside. In North America it grows from Florida to Georgia on rich soils in river valleys; in Europe it is planted in parks and streets. It thrives in partial shade and is damaged by severe frosts. It was introduced in Britain in 1726.

A greater height, more than 100 ft, is attained by the Western Catalpa *C. speciosa*, which has long-pointed leaves, larger flowers and a capsule twice as thick as in the Indian Bean. It is also a native of river valleys in the eastern United States. It is a sun-loving, fast-growing tree. In central and western Europe it is damaged by frost and is cultivated only rarely.

Common Ash

Fraxinus excelsior

The Common Ash is a deciduous tree 100 to 115 ft tall, with a long, straight, slender trunk. In winter it is distinguished by the black, globose buds growing in pairs, in summer by the odd-pinnately compound leaves composed of nine to thirteen lanceolate, serrate leaflets, 2 to 4 in. long. The male, female or bisexual flowers, without calyx or corolla, appear before the leaves unfold; they are pollinated by the wind. The elongate, oval, winged fruits (samaras) ripen in August and hang on the tree in bunches which persist long into the winter. Seed is produced about the thirtieth year and thereafter, there is a good crop almost every year, so that propagation is assured. The wood is of a pale colour, tough and elastic, and is used to make sports equipment and furniture.

The Ash is widely distributed throughout all of southern and central Europe, the northern boundary of its range extending from England through Scandinavia to Leningrad and the Volga. It grows in mixed lowland forests, alongside streams and on scree high up into the mountains. It needs abundant moisture and fertile soil and when full grown requires abundant light. It makes a good ornamental tree in parks and avenues.

The Manna Ash *F. ornus*, a native of southern Europe and western Asia, reaches a height of only 25 to 40 ft, and in central and western Europe is sometimes cultivated in warm situations in parks. The flowers are whitish and the winged fruits about half as large as those of the Common Ash. The bark of this tree, when cut, yields a liquid called "manna", which is used in pharmacy.

Of the North American species, those most often grown in Europe, are the White Ash *F. americana* and Red Ash *F. pennsylvanica*. Both have odd-pinnately compound leaves consisting of five to nine leaflets, brown buds and winged fruits which are narrower than those of the Common Ash. The White Ash is taller (up to 130 ft) than the Red Ash; its leaves and twigs are glabrous and the wing of the fruit is not decurrent. In the Red Ash twigs and leaves are densely hairy and the wing of the fruit is decurrent nearly to the base.

INDEX

Abies alba 26
– *balsamea* 28
– *cephalonica* 26
– *concolor* 28
– *grandis* 28
– *homolepis* 26
– *nordmanniana* 26
– *procera* 28
– *veitchii* 26
Acacia, False 104
Acer campestre 116
– *negundo* 118
– *palmatum* 118
– *platanoides* 116
– *pseudoplatanus* 116
– *rubrum* 118
– *saccharinum* 118
– *saccharum* 118
Aesculus carnea 120
– *hippocastanum* 120
– *octandra* 120
– *pavia* 120
Ailanthus altissima 110
Alder, Common 62,
– Grey 62
– Smooth 62
Alnus glutinosa 62
– *incana* 62
– *rugosa* 62
Apricot 98
Araucaria araucana 24
Arbor-vitae, American 48
– Chinese or Oriental 48
– Western or Giant 48
Arbutus menziesii 96
– *unedo* 96
Ash, Common 130
– Manna 130
– Mountain 92
– Red 130
– White 130
Aspen 52

Balm of Gilead 64
Bay, Bull 78
– Sweet 78
Beech, American 66
– Common or European 66
Betula lenta 60
– *lutea* 60
– *nigra* 60
– *papyrifera* 60
– *pendula* 60
– *pubescens* 60
Birch, Canoe 60
– Cherry 60
– Common 60
– River 60
– Silver 60
– Yellow 60
Bitternut 58
Blackthorn 98
Box-elder 118

Broom, Purple 106
Broussonetia papyrifera 76
Buckeye Red 120
– Sweet 120
Buckthorn, Alder 82
– Purging 82
Butternut 56
Buttonwood 84

Carpinus betulus 64
Carya cordiformis 58
– *glabra* 58
– *laciniosa* 58
– *ovata* 58
– *tomentosa* 58
Castanea crenata 68
– *dentata* 68
– *mollissima* 68
– *sativa* 68
Catalpa, Western 128
Catalpa bignonioides 128
– *speciosa* 128
Cedar, Atlantic 40
– Atlantic White 48
– Deodar 40
Cedar of lebanon 40
Cedrus atlantica 40
– *deodara* 40
– *libani* 40
Celtis occidentalis 74
Cercis canadensis 108
– *siliquastrum* 108
Chamaecyparis lawsoniana 48
– *nootkatensis* 48
– *obtusa* 48
– *pisifera* 48
– *thyoides* 48
Cherry, Bird 100
– Black 100
– Cornelian 124
– Mahaleb 100
– Sour 98
– Wild 98
Cherry Laurel 100
Chestnut, American 68
– Chinese 68
– Horse 118
– Japanese 68
– Sweet 68
China Tree 82
Cladrastris lutea 102
Cornus florida 124
– *mas* 124
– *sanguinea* 124
Cottonwood, Black 52
– Northern 52
Crataegus crus-galli 94
– *lavallei* 94
– *monogyna* 94
– *oxyacanthoides* 94
– *pubescens* 94
– *punctata* 94
Crab, Purple 88

Crab Wild 88
– Apple 88
Cucumber Tree 78
Cupressus macrocarpa 46
– *sempervirens* 46
Cypress, Common Swamp or Bald 50
– Hinoki 48
– Italian 46
– Lawson 48
– Monterey 46
– Nootka 48
– Sawara 48
Cytisus purpureus 106

Diospyros ebenum 126
– *kaki* 126
– *virginiana* 126
Dogwood, Flowering 124
– Red 122

Ebony, True 126
Elm, European White 74
– Smooth 74
– White 74
– Wych 74

Fagus grandifolia 66
– *sylvatica* 66
Fir, Balsam 28
– Douglas 32
– European Silver 26
– Giant 28
– Greek 26
– Nikko 26
– Noble 28
– Nordmann 26
– Veitch's Silver 26
– White 28
Firethorn, Common 94
Frangula alnus 82
Fraxinus americana 130
– *excelsior* 130
– *ornus* 130
– *pennsylvanica* 130

Gean 98
Ginkgo 20
Ginkgo biloba 20
Gleditschia triacanthos 108
Golden-chain or Golden-rain 106

Hackberry 74
Hawthorn, Common 94
– Midland 94
Hemlock, Eastern or Canadian 34
– Ground 22
– Mountain 34
– Western 34
Hickory, Big Shellbark 58
– Mockernut 58

Hickory Shagbark 58
Holly, American 114
– Common or English 114
Hop-hornbeam, American 64
– European 64
Hornbeam, Common 64
Horse Chestnut, Common 120
– Red 120

Ilex aquifolium 114
– *opaca* 114
Indian Bean 128

Judas Tree 108
Juglans cinerea 56
– *nigra* 56
– *regia* 56

Kaya, Japanese 24
Koelreuteria paniculata 82

Laburnocytisus adami 106
Laburnum, Common 106
– Scotch 106
Laburnum alpinum 106
– *anagyroides* 106
Larch, Dunkeld 36
– Eastern 36
– European 36
– Golden 38
– Japanese 26
Larix decidua 36
– *eurolepis* 36
– *leptolepis* 36
– *laricina* 36
Lime, American 122
– Common 122
– Large-leaved 122
– Silver 122
– Small-leaved 122
Linden 122
Liriodendron tulipifera 80
Locust, Black 104
– Clammy 104
– Honey 108

Maackia amurensis 102
Maclura pomifera 76
Madrona 124
Magnolia, Laurel 78
– Soulange 78
– Umbrella 78
Magnolia acuminata 78
– *denudata* 78
– *grandiflora* 78
– *liliflora* 78
– *x soulangiana* 78
– *stellata* 78
– *tripetala* 78
– *virginiana* 78
Maidenhair Tree 20
Malus x atrosanguinea 88
– *floribunda* 88
– *halliana* 88
– *prunifolia* 88
– *pumila* 88
Malus x purpurea 88
– *sieboldii* 88
– *sylvestris* 88
Maple, Ash-leaved 118
– Common 116
– Japanese 118
– Norway 118
– Red 118
– Silver 118
– Sugar 118
Monkey Puzzle 24
Morus alba 76
– *nigra* 76
– *rubra* 76
Mountain Ash 92
– American 92
Mulberry, Black 76
– Paper 76
– Red 76
– White 76

Nutmeg, California 24

Oak, Black 72
– Bur 70
– Common 70
– Durmast 70
– Holm 70
– Pin 72
– Red 72
– Scarlet 72
– Turkey 70
– White 70
Osage-orange 76
Osier, Common 54
– Purple 54
Ostrya carpinifolia 64
– *virginiana* 64

Peach 98
Pear, Snow 86
– Wild 86
– Willow-leaved 86
Persimmon, Chinese 16
– Common 126
Picea abies 30
– *omorika* 30
– *orientalis* 30
– *pungens* 30
– *sitchensis* 30
Pignut 58
Pine, Arolla 44
– Austrian 42
– Corsican 42
– Eastern White 44
– Himalayan 44
– Jack 42
– Lodgepole 42
– Macedonian 44
– Scots 42
– Stone 42
– Swiss Stone 44
– Weymouth 44
Pinus banksiana 42
– *cembra* 44
– *contorta* 42
Pinus nigra 42
– *peuce* 44
– *pinea* 42
– *strobus* 44
– *sylvestris* 42
– *wallichiana* 44
Plane, American 84
– London 84
– Oriental 84
Platanus x hybrida 84
– *occidentalis* 84
– *orientalis* 84
Plum 98
Poplar, Balsam 52
– Black or Lombardy 52
– Carolina 52
– Western Balsam 52
– White 52
Populus alba 52
– *balsamifera* 52
– *canadensis* 52
– *deltoides* 52
– *gileadensis* 52
– *nigra* 52
– *tremula* 52
– *trichocarpa* 52
Pride of India 82
Prunus armeniaca 98
– *avium* 98
– *cerasus* 98
– *domestica* 98
– *laurocerasus* 100
– *mahaleb* 100
– *padus* 100
– *persica* 100
– *serotina* 100
– *spinosa* 98
Pseudolarix amabilis 38
Pseudotsuga glauca 32
– *menziesii* 32
Pterocarya flaxinifolia 58
Pyracantha coccinea 94
Pyrus communis 86
– *nivalis* 86
– *salicifolia* 86

Quercus alba 70
– *cerris* 70
– *coccinea* 72
– *ilex* 70
– *marcrocarpa* 70
– *palustris* 72
– *petraea* 70
– *robur* 70
– *rubra* 72
– *velutina* 72

Redbud, Eastern 108
Redwood 50
Rhamnus cathartica 82
Rhus coriaria 112
– *typhina* 112
– *verniciflua* 112
Robinia pseudacacia 104
– *viscosa* 104
Rowan 92

Salix alba 54
– *babylonica* 54
– *caprea* 54
– *fragilis* 54
– *purpurea* 54
– *triandra* 54
– *viminalis* 54
Sallow, Great 54
Sequoia, Giant 50
Sequoia sempervirens 50
Sequoiadendron giganteum 50
Service Tree 92
– Wild 90
Sloe 98
Snowball, Japanese 126
Sorbus americana 92
– *aria* 90
– *aucuparia* 92
– *domestica* 92
– *latifolia* 90
– *torminalis* 90
Spruce, Colorado or Blue 30
– Common or Norway 30
– Oriental 30
– Serbian 30
– Sitka 30
Strawberry Tree 96
Styrax japonica 96
Sumach, Staghorn 112
Sycamore 116

Tamarack 36
Taxodium distichum 50
Taxus baccata 22
– *canadensis* 22
– *cuspidata* 22
Thorn, Cockspur 94
– Dotted 94
– Lavallee's 94
– Mexican 94
Thuja occidentalis 48
– *orientalis* 48
– *plicata* 48
Tilia americana 122
– *cordata* 122
– *platyphyllos* 122
– *tomentosa* 122
– *vulgaris* 122
Torreya californica 24
– *nucifera* 24
Tree of Heaven 110
Tsuga canadensis 34
– *heterophylla* 34
– *mertensiana* 34
Tulip Tree 80

Ulmus americana 74
– *glabra* 74
– *laevis* 74
– *minor* 74

Varnish Tree 112

Walnut, Black 56
– Common 56
Wellingtonia 50
Whitebeam 90
– Broad-leaved 90
Willow, Almond-leaved 54
– Crack 54
– Cricket-bat 54
– Goat 54
– Weeping 54
– White 54
Wingnut, Caucasian 58

Yellow-wood 102
Yew, Canadian 22
– Common or English 22
– Japanese 22

Zelkova carpinifolia 74